CLASSICS OF RUSSIAN POETRY

Pushkin

EUGENE ONEGIN

"Translators are the post-horses of civilization."
A. S. Pushkin (1830)

by the same author

Pasternak	POEMS (University of Michigan Press, 1959)
Pasternak	POEMS (The Antioch Press, 1964) Second Edition, revised and enlarged.
Pushkin	EUGENE ONEGIN

forthcoming

Pushkin	LITTLE TRAGEDIES
Shchipachev	POEMS OF LABOR AND LOVE
Lermontov	THE DEMON & OTHER POEMS
Pushkin	THE BRONZE HORSEMAN & OTHER POEMS
Pushkin	TSAR SALTAN & OTHER FOLK TALES

ALEXANDER PUSHKIN

Eugene Onegin
A Novel in Verse

translated from the Russian
by Eugene M. Kayden

illustrated by N. V. Kuzmin

The Antioch Press
Yellow Springs, Ohio • 1964

Acknowledgments

The translation is based on the definitive Russian text edited by Boris Victorovich Tomashevsky, published by the Institute of Literature, Academy of Science of USSR, Moscow-Leningrad, 1949.

The selected illustrations by N. V. Kuzmin are taken from the edition of 'Eugene Onegin' published by ACADEMIA in 1933. The translator is sincerely grateful to the Foreign Languages Publishing House, Moscow, for the permission to reproduce a number of pen drawings.

DEDICATED TO

JOHN FITZGERALD KENNEDY

PRESIDENT OF THE UNITED STATES OF AMERICA

BUILDER OF PEACE AND FRIENDSHIP

BETWEEN NATIONS AND RACES

In Memoriam

Contents

Foreword

NEARLY five generations have passed since Pushkin's death in 1837. In every generation men have cried out against his seeming apartness from the burning issues of the day; yet, in every generation, conservative and liberal, monarchist and socialist alike have been moved to tears over lines of Pushkin because of their truth, beauty, and grace. This veneration of Pushkin can be understood only by those who see true religion as a worship of life and freedom, unconfused by prevailing social and moral notions, as the startled cry of the human soul wakened to a world of haunted wonder. Pushkin had none of that narrow intelligence which makes for leadership in a movement; to him, life was older than propaganda and reform and art more central than political philosophy or aesthetic doctrine.

Pushkin was the first Russian to understand the unalterable religious instinct of the people as manifested in their sense of love and all-embracing compassion, their humility, their practical wisdom of life, and their capacity to yield what is dear and beloved for a common cause. And he made their moral conscience his own—conscience, and not proud disdain and revolt as the restorer of universal sympathy and order. He was a truly universal poet, one without the weight of pretentious seriousness, romantic revolt, and oracular utterance, a poet profound in the power of his amazing receptivity and the range of his bounteous, tolerant humanity. In serving his vision of the truth, Pushkin inspired generations of men in their struggle against privilege, corruption, and irresponsible power.

Pushkin, too, was the founder of that supreme art of Russian realism whose vital substance is devotion to the intimate and immediate truths of life, a plastic realism illumined by a sympathetic vision that sees each object in the external world complete in all its relationships. Like an echo, he responded to the life and enterprise of the world about him with all its hidden relations and contradictions, passing with lightness from despair to hope, from fun to prayer, from revolt to crooning of fairy-tales, this profuse variety of his created universe becoming one in him by some magic of peace and spiritual reconciliation which he carried within his own soul. The sensuous appeal of his imagination enhanced his work by figures of lovely motion, by a wealth of jeweled tones, by words always just and illuminating, words light and sparkling and words full and heavy as honey—till all the parts seemed to move together with the unity of a final thought as only great poetry is final. These qualities of expression have established Pushkin in the minds of his countrymen as the omni-human poet, as the unattainable ideal in the art of poetic composition.

How unattainable must be any translator's object to make Pushkin real in a foreign language! How vain must be the striving to translate his poetic form, assonance, nuances of diction, rhythms, idioms, rhymes, all of which in their totality make up the word-complex of his poetry! How profitless, too, is the struggle to conserve at the same time qualities of plasticity and sound comprised in his lines of incomparable beauty, sincerity, and simplicity!

However, translations are necessary and inevitable. Translators, in the words of Pushkin, are "the post-horses of civilization." Be it also remembered that each language is an independent instrument, exempt from arbitrary control, each with a logic of its own and bearing within itself echoes of historic culture and tradition. The difficulties of translation are naturally exceptional: It is not easy to have a version faithful to the original, and yet catch in English the very intonations of the poet's voice and the grace of his appeal. It is heartening to recall the defense of translation made in the preface to the King James version of the Bible: "Translation it is that openeth the window, to let in the light; that breaketh the shell, that we may eat the kernel; that putteth aside the curtain, that we may look into the most Holy place; that removeth the cover of the well, that we may come by the water, even as Jacob rolled away the stone from the mouth of the well, by which means the flocks of Laban were watered. Indeed without translation . . . the unlearned are but like children at Jacob's well (which was deep) without a bucket or something to draw with."

Among translators and, more especially, among their critics, there are those who believe that a translation of Pushkin should respect the formula of the stanza first and last, and should keep the rhyme scheme of masculine and feminine pairs in which the lines are articulated, without a single deviation. The price is heavy for such an endeavor and is always obvious in the extent of free paraphrasing, graceless padding, unserviceable inversions—infidelities hard to keep down and harder to keep out. At the other extreme there are those who insist upon literal versions and line-by-line translations. In the minds of their critics, such equivalents are false to the nature of poetry itself, false to the logic of words distinguishing one language from another. Such baldly literal translations appear as unfaithful to poetry as paraphrases do.

Some twenty years ago, at the beginning of my work on *Eugene Onegin*, I tried at first to adhere faithfully to the strictly unvarying pattern of Pushkin's stanza. I tried also a line-by-line prose translation. I persevered in both cases for two chapters, but finally gave up these plans as a juggler's craft. There is no satisfaction in the knowledge that feminine rhymes may be found in the English version wherever they occur in the original, whatever the cost in truth and precision in the recipient language. I wanted something more direct and faithful in meaning and faultlessness, yet poetical as English—a prose distinguishable from the prose of the street and the classroom, a form of common speech made transcendent by the imagination.

In my present translation, completed in the spring of 1960, I have been faithful to Pushkin's rhythmic stanza, modified only in the employment of masculine and feminine rhymes in the twelve lines forming the three quatrains, but unchanged in the two concluding lines that form the coda. I hold that a translation of poetry must be poetry in English and have therefore preferred to preserve the tone and sweep of *Eugene Onegin* at the price of three pairs of rhymes in each stanza.

Formal adherence to a rhyming scheme is not a serious problem of exaggeration in Russian; in English, it is a misadventure. In English, rhymes are far less unobtrusive; yet English can win and maintain its truest power regardless of chiming versification. I hold that English can say most about Russian poetry when it is most like itself—faithful to its own genius.

Above all, the translator is a poet's fellow adventurer in realms of spiritual being. His function is truly creative. He is the bridge between different nations and races. Such a bridge is of special importance today if we are to have fruitful cultural relations in a world of conflicting ideologies and interests. This age of ours, richer in new sources of wealth and power for good or evil than any other age of the past, demands from the poet both a deeper comprehension of human cultures and greater courage in serving his vision of the truth, if we are to have peace and freedom in a world so tragically small and defenseless. There are signs on all sides that humanity is entering— even through strife and death—into a new kingdom of thought and truth. The mission of the poet is therefore a voyage of discovery in the unknown future, and he serves humanity best by giving to his own nation the gift of self. We need the exalted vision of the poet in modern life, who can speak for his people without fumbling or hesitation, and next to the poet, the translator's art.

We need, too, the exalted vision of the statesman who will speak for art in the name of man in a world-wide community of nations. "I see little of more importance to the future of our country and our civilization," said President Kennedy at ground-breaking for the Robert Frost Library, "than full recognition of the place of the artist. If art is to nourish the roots of our culture, society must set the artist free"—in service to his vision of truth and the nation.

EUGENE M. KAYDEN

Introduction

*by Vissarion Belinsky**

I CONFESS is is not without a certain diffidence that I am
embarking upon a critical examination of such a poetic work
as *Eugene Onegin*. It was Pushkin's most beloved work and
the dearest child of his imagination. Few literary works reflect
the individuality of the poet as fully and as clearly as *Eugene
Onegin* mirrors Pushkin. His whole life appears in this poem,—
his love, his soul, the fullness of his emotions, conceptions,
and ideals. Apart from its artistic merits, it has for Russians
great historical and social significance. First of all, it imagina-
tively recreates Russian society in one of its most interesting
periods of cultural development. From this angle alone, it is
an historical poem in the fullest sense of the word even
though not a single historical person appears in the narrative.
The historical merit is all the more significant in that it
was the first and most brilliant achievement of its kind in
Russian literature. Thus Pushkin is here not only the poet
but also the spokesman for a newly-awakened social consciousness. That his work is still not generally accepted as
truly national is due to the strange belief that a Russian man
in a frock-coat or a Russian woman in stays is not really
Russian, that the true type must be sought in an environment
of bast sandals, homebrew, and cabbage soup.

It is time for readers to understand that a Russian poet
may reveal himself as genuinely national when he sets forth
the life and progress of the educated social classes, provided
he is a man of talent and is national at heart. "Genuine
nationality," said Gogol, "consists not in a description of
peasant dress but in the manifestation of the spirit of the
people, for a poet may be national even when he is describing

*Translated directly from the Russian. Readers are referred to the last
section, "Notes and Comments," for information about Belinsky and the
poem itself.—E.M.K.

a world entirely alien to himself but a world which he beholds through the eyes of the whole nation and when he feels and speaks in a way which makes his countrymen believe that it is they themselves who are thus feeling and speaking." He who can grasp only the stark common life of the masses without grasping the more subtle and complex traits of historic life will never be a great poet and certainly not a national poet.

In accordance with this concept, the first artistic truly-national work was Pushkin's *Eugene Onegin*. The determination of the young poet to present the moral aspects of Russia's most Europeanized social estate offers clear proof that he considered himself a national poet. He understood that the day of epic poetry had long since passed and that, to portray modern society, a writer must employ as his medium the novel and not the epic tale. Pushkin used life about him as he found it in its totality, including its elements of banality and violence. Such a bold design would have been less surprising had his romance been written in prose. To have conceived that romance in verse, at a time when there was not even in prose a single worthwhile Russian novel, was a feat of literary daring vindicated only by its amazing success and the undeniable fact of poetic genius.

It was Lord Byron who can rightfully be said to have created the style and manner of the romance in verse in his medley of prose and poetry, the use of digressions, the resort to soliloquizing, and especially the intrusion of the poet himself into his work. All that was truly Byronic. However, the romances of the two poets have only form and treatment in common. Both the contents and the spirit of Byron preclude all possibility of establishing any essential similarity between his and Pushkin's work. Byron wrote about Europe for Europeans: his subjective spirit, so profound and impressive, and his personality, so wondrously proud and indomitable, aspired not so much to demonstrate contemporary mankind as to pronounce upon man's past and present history. But Pushkin wrote about Russian realities for Russians. The manifestation and wonder of his original genius lie in the fact that Pushkin, true to his nature—a nature diametrically opposed to that of Byron—and to his artistic instinct, was never tempted to create anything Byronic when he wrote his novel in verse. Had he done so, his readers would have glorified him without end, and fame, total though evanescent, would have been his popular reward for such a spurious *tour de force*. But Pushkin was too extraordinary a poet for such a harlequinade, a performance alluring only to poets of inferior talent. Pushkin had no wish to imitate Byron; his concern was to be himself and to be true to reality, to all the undiscovered social facts in the Russian world. That is the reason why his *Eugene Onegin* is a supremely original creation of national life.

The story of Onegin is too well known to require a detailed analysis. A brief outline will suffice. Tatyána, a young girl brought up in the seclusion of the countryside and devoted to the romances of her time, falls in love at first sight with a young St. Petersburg aristocrat, who, bored by social life in the city, has come down to his inherited country estate to while away the tedious days. Tatyána, breathless with her naive passion, writes him a letter confessing her love. Onegin replies verbally that he cannot love her and that he does not consider himself made for family happiness. Onegin is then challenged to a duel over a trivial incident by Lensky, the fiance of Tatyána's sister. Lensky is killed and his death separates Onegin and Tatyána for a few years. Disillusioned by her youthful dream of love, she yields to the pleadings and tears of her old mother and marries a wealthy general; it matters not to her whom she marries since she must marry someone. Years later Onegin meets Tatyána at a soirée and hardly recognizes her, so changed she is and so little resemblance does the once simple country girl bear to the grand Petersburg lady. Onegin falls desperately in love with the new Tatyána and writes her a letter confessing his passion. Tatyána tells him directly that, although she still loves him, she cannot belong to him—through pride of virtue and duty.

Most readers of the romance—a story without a denouement of any kind—have held that Onegin had no heart or soul and that he was callous and cold, an egoist by nature. There can be no more mistaken view of the man. Many have accepted too carelessly the belief that the poet purposefully partrayed Onegin as an unfeeling egoist. That judgment amounts to one's having eyes but seeing nothing. Life in high society had not destroyed Onegin's feelings but rather had made him hate a life of barren passions and idle pleasures. Onegin was not an ordinary man by nature. His aspirations for a better life speak more of feeling than of emotional aridity and indifference. He was not a man addicted to day-dreaming; he felt more than he could express in words, for he did not bare his heart to everyone. An embittered mind is often the symptom of a higher nature, for such a man is usually displeased not only with other men but with himself as well; ordinary men are most frequently pleased with themselves, and, if they are in luck, with everybody else. Disillusionment with life, society, and self (if it is genuine and simple, and not couched in phrases of romantic sadness) is an attribute of those men who demand much of life and are satisfied with nothing less. It was not his nature, passions, or his delusions that had made Onegin indifferent and bored. His social environment and the age in which he was reared and in which he lived had brought about his disenchantment.

Onegin is neither Melmoth nor Childe Harold, neither demon, parody, nor genius, but he is simply a plain good fellow, though an uncommon one. He does not know what he wants or what he is after, but he does know only too well that he does not care for the things that give delight and contentment to the smug, the insensitive, and the trivial people about him. The smug have without real insight declared him to be immoral and have deprived him of passions of the heart, ardor of the soul, and the enjoyment of what is good and beautiful.

In an analysis of Onegin's character, I have thus far refrained from describing him as an egoist. However, since surfeit of feeling and craving for the beautiful do not exclude egoism, Onegin may be identified as a suffering egoist, an egoist despite himself. Why did Onegin not find satisfaction in useful, salutary, beneficial social activity, and contentment in the going affairs of life? It is easier to ask questions than to find the right answers. It is not impossible to find useful activity under normal social conditions. But what could Onegin have achieved within the framework of social standards popular among feudal landowners? To lighten the burden of the peasant serfs might have meant a great deal to the peasants, but such a free gift was not sufficient to absorb Onegin's interest and could not keep him usefully occupied for a lifetime.

Separated from Tatyána by Lensky's death, Onegin lost his last link that bound him to human beings. To see all about him gaiety and sorrow, and laughter and tears, and yet consider himself a man alienated from society,—this is suffering few can understand but dreadful in its effects nevertheless. The more natural and unaffected Onegin's suffering, the less it could be apprehended by most. To have experienced so much at twenty-six without having accomplished anything and to have arrived at absolute negation without aims and convictions of any sort can only be defined as death. Yet Onegin was not fated to die without having tasted the cup of life to the dregs: a profound passion was not long in awakening the slumbering spiritual powers within his soul.

His letter to Tatyána is aflame with passion. Gone are the irony and the conventional restraints, the fear of social gossip, malice, or ridicule. Outwardly, Tatyána appears to have resigned herself to a life of worldly vanity; if that had been true, Onegin's role would have been very ludicrous and pitiful indeed. But Onegin would have been justified in taking it for granted that Tatyána had remained essentially true to her nature and that polite society had merely taught her the art of self-command. In what light, then, would Tatyána have appeared to Onegin—Tatyána who was no longer the romantic simple girl, confiding her cherished thoughts to the moon and stars, but a woman who knew the value of her spiritual essence, a woman who would demand much but one who would also give a great deal? The glory of Tatyána's social success could not have exalted her in Onegin's eyes. In society, as everywhere else, despite the vulgarity of some elements, there are those who are rich in the knowledge of life and people and who possess the faculty of completely mastering all that nature has bestowed upon them. Such a person was Tatyána. Her importance as a lady of quality merely enhanced her essential womanliness. Moreover, to Onegin, love without a struggle was bereft of sweetness and Tatyána held out no promise of an easy conquest. Even so, Onegin threw himself into the struggle without hope of victory, without forethought, but with all the bewilderment of a sincere passion.

The romance ends with Tatyána's rebuff to Onegin: Did his existence end in lifeless apathy, or was his spirit purged and reborn in new suffering? What need has one to know the answers to these questions? It suffices to know that his richly-endowed nature remained without serious application and his life without aim or meaning. It is enough to know that Onegin might have been happy or unhappy under conditions of free choice and the fullest use of his abundant capacity for work.

Aside from the characters of Onegin and Lensky, it is Pushkin's great merit that he was the first to present in this romance an ideal portrait of Russian womanhood in its historical development. In this world of morally-warped phenomena, as they affect the life of women in the family and society, there are rare and happy exceptions, individuals who pay dearly for their inner spiritual independence. But they are unfortunately the victims of their own superior endowment; as natures of genius they are relentlessly sacrificed by an unconscious society as an offering to its own shortcomings. Such a nature was that of Tatyána. It is by no means easy to define her character. It was not complex, but it was deep, intense, cohesive. She was made compact of a piece, without any admixtures; her life was interfused by that sort of integrity and unity, which, in the world of art, constitutes the highest degree of perfection.

A passionately-infatuated, simple country girl of seventeen, later a lady of fashion, Tatyána is always the same in her wholesome candor and integrity. Her childhood portrait, described by the poet with such absolute mastery, was subsequently touched up but not essentially altered in its lineaments. For her, love could be either a great blessing or a real misfortune. Given the joy of reciprocity, the love of such a woman is like a steady bright flame; failing reciprocity, it is a stubborn flame, destructive all the more for being pent up and controlled from breaking out perhaps only by strength of will. Such is Tatyána's character.

A human being is created by nature but is developed and formed by forces existing in the structure of society. No circumstances of life can safeguard a person from the influences at work in society. The very endeavor of a person to develop independently of society results in forms of singularity or freakishness. (That is the reason why gifted people, richly endowed by nature, are often unbearable in their relations to others.) When life and idealism are in conflict, when these two forces lack a natural vital bond of coherence and unity, their separate existence gives rise to a spuriously idealistic and morbid condition. Therefore, those who feel keenly the existing disharmony devise for themselves an imaginative ideal existence. Finding no idealism operative in society, they take their idealism from books. If idealism says that love is the essence and soul of life (as did Rousseau's), the conclusion follows that one must love with heart and mind; thus the ideal youth or maid must seek an object with which to fall in love.

Tatyána did not escape the sad fate of the ideal young woman. Her character was indeed exceptional. Her deep and passionate nature overshadowed whatever there was in her of any ludicrous ideality, including even her naive beliefs and folk prejudices. Tatyána's entire inner world consisted of her intense craving for love; her soul responded to nothing else but that. Her mind was still unawakened; only profound disillusionment could have awakened her mind, merely to restrain her passion and subordinate it to dictates of conventional social morality. Except for the sentimental books she read, she would have been an utterly inarticulate creature. There are women whose imagination wields much greater influence on the heart than it is generally believed to do. Tatyána was such a woman.

The story of Tatyána's hopeless anguish is told with wonderful simplicity and fidelity. Her visits to Onegin's deserted home and the emotions awakened within her by every object that bore the imprint of his spirit and character form some of the finest passages of the poem. Generally speaking, unrequited love which stubbornly survives all hope is a rather morbid phenomenon whose origin would appear to be located in the exalted imagination; the suffering originating in the imagination falls heavily upon the heart, tormenting it sometimes with even greater force than the sufferings which are rooted within the heart itself. By reading with care Onegin's books, Tatyána experienced a redeeming act of consciousness. Her mind had awakened. At least she understood that a person has anxieties and sorrows beyond those of love only. But did she understand precisely what they were? If she did, did her new knowledge help to mitigate her own sufferings? No doubt she understood them but with her mind alone; her bookish acquaintance with the new world of sorrows, though it may have served as a revelation to Tatyána, made only a painful impression. It startled her, horrified her; it persuaded her as to the necessity of submitting to reality as found in fact. It made her realize that, if one was to live the life of the heart, one had to keep it to oneself, to guard it in the depths of one's own spirit, in the stillness of seclusion and in the dark of night given to grief and tears. Her visits to Onegin's house and the reading of his books prepared Tatyána for her transformation,—from an unawakened simple country girl into a lady of society who so amazed Onegin.

It is Tatyána's last meeting with Onegin that reveals best

this changed person, all the elements that constitute the real essence of the Russian woman: her profound social nature, ardent passion, sincerity of deep-felt emotions, the purity of naive impulses, sense of injured vanity and outraged virtue. She begins with a reproach: Onegin, she avers, was in fact to blame because he had not loved her then when she was 'younger and better.' Such were her conceptions, borrowed from weak sentimental novels! But her reproaches are instantly followed by an exoneration: her rebuke consists in her conviction that Onegin had not loved her earlier merely because there had been no lure of temptation for him, whereas now it was the thirst of conquest that was driving him on. Her words reveal her fear lest her good name be blemished in society but also her real contempt for the class she now belongs to, associations she would gladly surrender for the peace of the country, her shelf of books, the simple rural life of her youth.

Eugene Onegin was composed over a period of eight years. In the persons of Onegin and Tatyána, Pushkin has portrayed Russian society in a period of its greatest cultural development with uncommon fullness, faithfulness, and art, on many levels of life and nature. The poet's digressions and informal discourses abound with ineffable charm, sincerity, emotion, intellect, and wit. Everywhere one is conscious of a poet wholly loving and humane; his very satire mirrors much affection; his very negation not infrequently resembles tolerance and even admiration,—all out of his great love for life and people.

Eugene Onegin may be designated as an encyclopedia of Russian life and as a supremely national achievement in all its phases of composition. The poem exercised a profound influence on contemporary and subsequent Russian literature. It was essentially a deed of social consciousness for all Russia and constituted almost the first and greatest word in the name of life and literature. After its publication, there could no longer be any question of standing still. Time will pass and bring in its wake new ideals and other problems, new needs and fresh works, and Russian society will grow and even surpass Pushkin's masterpiece. But however far society may advance, the Russian people will forever love and revere their poet and his masterpiece. The following lines, so befitting as a conclusion to our essay, speak of his hopes in a way more direct and eloquent than words of our own invention:

"I live nor write for praise, but fear
To die unknown in fame and story.
I'd rather win a little place
For my sad name, some share of glory,
One note,—one line of poetry,
That, like a friend, shall speak for me.

"Perhaps my lines a stranger's heart
May move; perhaps, by luck or fate,
At last dark Lethe will not swallow
The stanzas I today create.
Perhaps (what overweening hope!)
A simple fellow may some day
Point to my portrait and declare:
'He was a poet, a man of scope!'
O lover of the peaceful Muses,
Receive my thanks and salutation,—
O dearest friend, whose memory
Will shrine my fugitive creation,
Whose hand of grace may yet caress
An old man's bays with tenderness."

. . . let me introduce to you
The hero of my tale,—that true
Old friend of mine, Eugene Onegin.

Pétri de vanité il avait encore plus de cette espèce d'orgueil qui fait avouer avec la même indifférence les bonnes comme les mauvaises actions, suite d'un sentiment de supériorité, peut-être imaginaire.

Tiré d'une lettre particulière.

DEDICATION

Not moved by craving to delight
The haughty public but to please
You as a friend, I'd like to write
Some pages worthier than these—
More worthy of your noble mind,
Your days of living poetry,
Your dreams of service to mankind,
Your grace and true simplicity.
You will, I pray, accept with favor
This sheaf of chapters in your hand,—
Half-gay, half-sad, rich with the savor
Of simple tales and matter grand.
Receive this fruit of inspiration,
Of wakeful thought and ready art,
My dreams of faded youth apart,
My cold, impartial observation
And grievous insights of my heart.

Chapter One

He is in haste to live and in a wild hurry to feel.
Prince Vyázemsky

I

"My uncle was the soul of honor[1]
And, when at last he took to bed,
He had the sense to make his kin
Respect his smallest wish, in dread
Before his disapproving gaze.
But Lord above! what fearful boredom
To tend the sick all day and night,
And never move away for days!
What pitiful dissimulation
A dying man to entertain,—
Arrange the pillows for his head,
Prepare his medicine, then feign
A sigh of grief, and wonder why
The devil takes his time to die."

2

Thus mused the youthful rascal, flying
Post-haste through summer dust and glare,
Who by the gods supreme was fated
To be his relative's sole heir.
But let me introduce to you,
O friends of Lyudmíla and Ruslán,[2]
Without a word of explanation
The hero of my tale,—that true
Old friend of mine, Eugene Onegin.
He lived through all his life beside
The Neva shores where you perhaps
Were born and flourished in your pride.
I used to like that place of old
But found its climate somewhat cold.[3]

3

His father served the State with honor
But lived in debt like a gentleman;
He gave three balls each winter season
And ended up a bankrupt man.
The fates, however, saved the child
Thanks to the kindness of *Madame*,
His watchful nurse, and then *Monsieur*.
The boy was lovable, but wild.
Monsieur l'abbé, the needy tutor,
Refused to tire his childish brain
With lessons, given half in fun
Each day, or reprimand in vain
His charge for every boyish lark
While playing in the Summer Park.

4

But when Eugene had reached the time
Of restless youth, with dreams aglow,
The age of hope and tender yearning,
Monsieur was told that he must go.
And then Onegin, trimmed and curled
With care in fashion's latest style
And dressed up like a London dandy,
At last was ready for the world.
His French was generally perfect
In letters and in conversation;
He danced with grace and learned to bow
Without a trace of affectation,
And all agreed he was a prize,
A very nice young man and wise.

5

We learn a little more or less
Somehow, at random, as we can,
And thus it's not too difficult
To seem an educated man.
Onegin was declared in truth
By men discerning in their judgments
To be a well-read fellow, though
A forward and presumptuous youth.[4]
He had the gift of touching on
A topic lightly with a dry
Remark, or listening in silence
To grave debates, then letting fly
A pun or epigram meanwhile
That always made the ladies smile.

6

Since Latin was no more in fashion,
His stock in that was small, yet quite
Enough to prate of Juvenal,
To puzzle mottoes out at sight,
To close a letter with the spell
Of *Vale*, or, faultily, to quote
A line or two of the *Aeneid*
He fancied he remembered well.
He had no antiquarian zeal
For digging in the dusty pages
Of long ago, but could recite
Familiar tales of other ages,—
Historic anecdotes and lays
From Romulus to modern days.[5]

7

He entertained no godlike passion
For poetry and lyric treasures;
Despite my pains, he still confused
Trochaic with iambic measures.
He damned Theocritus and great
Old Homer, liked his Adam Smith,
And was no mean economist:
That is, he could elucidate
How modern states expand by trade
In wealth and power, and why, if sold,
Their raw commodities are more
Reliable than hoarded gold.
His father failed to understand
And kept on mortgaging his land.

8

The scope of all Onegin's learning
I cannot possibly impart
For lack of time, but I can say
He mastered well one special art:
It was his earnest occupation,
His joy, his torment from his youth,
Exacting days of care and leisure,
Of idle pining and vexation,—
The art of love and gallantry
That Ovid once immortalized
And for it ended his career
In exile, by the world despised,
Alone beside the Euxine Sea
Afar from home and Italy.

(9) 10

Onegin learned to mask his feelings,
The studied art of make-believe;
To languish, mute with jealousy,
Or grieve with hope—and undeceive;
To seem by turns indifferent,
Attentive, haughty in his bearing;
To be completely taciturn
Or passionately eloquent.
How artless were his notes avowing
Undying love, his blissfulness!
Deep moving in his self-surrender,
His eyes grew soft with tenderness
Or shone with daring, hurt, or fears,
Or glistened with complaisant tears.

11

How shrewdly he could play the novice
Before the young or jestingly
Affright them with his feigned despair
And snare their hearts with flattery,
Then seize the hour of tenderness
For overcoming maiden fear
By passion and disarming skill!
How well he'd pray a shy caress,
Enjoy the rapture of young love
And innocence, then still pursue
The object of his love—to win
A moment's tender rendezvous,
Or in some secret nook apart
Instruct the lady of his heart.

12

How soon he learned the way to gladden
The heart of the confirmed coquette!
And, when he chose to crush a rival,
What traps and pitfalls he could set
To run him down and even take
Delight in sneers and calumny!
Yet men who lived in wedded bliss
Remained his friends: the married rake
Well-schooled in Faublas' strategy[6]
Who favored him with friendliness;
Suspicious, easy-going age;
The cuckold in his haughtiness
Completely satisfied with life—
Himself, his dinner, and his wife.

The cuckold in his haughtiness
Completely satisfied with life—
Himself, his dinner, and his wife.

13

(13, 14) 15

And then the daily invitations!
Before he's up, before he's dressed,
Three charming little notes—three notes—
Request him, please, to be their guest.
A children's party, or a dance,
Or a soirée: Which evening, where?
Which promises the best amusement?
He'll manage to accept perchance
All three. Meanwhile, in morning garb
And hatted *à la Bolivar*,[7]
He drives along the boulevard
Or saunters in the open air
Until his faithful *Breguet* chime[8]
Announces it is dinner-time.

16

At dusk a sleigh-ride is the thing.
Then to the driver's cry, "way-way!"
He speeds; his beaver collar's white
With starry flakes and silver spray.
He will at evening entertain
His friend Kavérin[9] at *Talon's*.[10]
They'll hail the lively pop of corks,
The spurt of 'Comet' fine champagne,
The tender roastbeef on the table,
And truffles, too—the choicest prize
And pleasure of the French cuisine,—
With fresh-imported Strasbourg pies,
A slice of seasoned Limburg cheese
And pineapples from overseas.

Onegin, Pushkin, Kaverin
at Talon's

Glass after glass—to wash the hot
Rich cutlets down! But the ballet,
His watch sonorously announces,
Must even now be under way.
This arbitrator, caustic sage
And critic, fickle worshipper
Of rising charming actresses,
And honored friend of the back-stage,—
Onegin flies now to the theatre.
There spectators are free to hiss
Their Cleopatra, Phèdre, or to cheer
New steps and turns; they never miss
To call Moïna[11] out—because
They're flattered by their own applause.

18[12]

O magic land! Our lord of satire,
Vonvízin, friend of liberty,
Shone here, and dramatist Knyazhnín
Resembled him in mimicry;
Here Ózerov was once the rage
And shared with young Semyónova
The tribute of the people's tears;
Katénin at a later stage
Restored Corneille to fuller glory,
And Shakhovskóy here came to stay
With his sardonic comedies;
Didelót earned too his crown of bay.
There, in the wings, in all their maze,
I whiled away my youthful days.

19

My Graces, where are you today?
I sadly call on each dear name.
Have other maidens filled your places?
Are you still charming, still the same?
And shall I see your choral dance
And hear you sing? behold your flight
Inspired, fair Russian Terpsichore?
Or will my melancholy glance
No more upon this dreary stage
Find one familiar face I've known,
But through my disenchanted glass
Look on, indifferent, alone?
Shall I in silence yawn, downcast,
And brood upon the splendid past?

20

Full theatre. The boxes glitter!
The stalls and pit—a humming cup;
The galleries, impatient, clap;
The curtain rustles, going up.
Ethereal, in light aglow,
With lovely nymphs about her circling,
To the magic of the viol strings
Istómina[13] spins upon her toe.
Her foot rests lightly on its tip
While languidly her body swings,
And, blown like down by Aeolus,
With a leap into the air she springs;
She twirls and wheels, lithe as a feather,
And claps in mid-air her heels together.

21

The crowds applaud. Between the stalls
Onegin treads on many a toe
While peering through his opera glass
At ladies whom he does not know.
He looks askance at every tier
And turns disdainfully away,
Displeased with people and their dress.
He nods his head to someone here
And there among close friends, in silence,
Then absently he scans the stage,
And, yawning, ridicules the scene:
"Old stuff! They lag behind the age!
I'm bored by their insipid show
And talk about their great Didelót!"

22

While flashing cupids, imps, and satyrs
Across the stage careen and soar,
And weary footmen doze beside
Their masters' fur coats at the door;
While still they stamp and hiss, or shout
Applause, or cough, or blow their noses;
While still inside and out of doors
The lanterns glitter all about;
While still the carriage-horses shiver
From cold, impatient at their stands,
And coachmen, crowded round the bonfire,
Cursing, try hard to warm their hands,
Onegin hurries through the press
For home—to change to evening dress.

23

How paint for your imagination
My hero's private rooms and den,
Where the prototype of modern fashion
Is dressed, undressed, and dressed again?
All that the trade of London brings
Across the Baltic salt sea waves
In exchange for tallow, wax, or timber,
To meet our whims for costly things;
All that the greedy crafts of Paris
As paying merchandise produce
To please our taste for luxuries
And modern objects for our use,
Adorned the bedroom of our keen
Philosopher at age eighteen.[14]

24

There china, porcelain, and bronzes,
And amber pipes were set with care,
And, to delight the pampered senses,
Perfumes in crystal vials rare;
All kinds of dainty files of steel
And combs and scissors, straight or curved,
And brushes of some thirty sizes
And shapes for teeth and nails. I feel
Rousseau—I say it but in passing—
Pretended not to understand
Why pompous Grimm[15] dared clean his nails
Before him—noblest firebrand:
For once the friend of liberties
And rights was surely hard to please.

25

A man of sense may pay attention
Even to the beauty of his nails.
Why fight one's own generation
Where autocratic rule prevails?
Onegin was in dress tiptop,
Like Chaadáyev.[16] Prim to a fault,
Precise in all details, he was
In fact a dandy and a fop.
Three mortal hours a day at least
He spent before his looking-glass,
Emerging from his dressing-room
In grace a Venus when she'd pass
At times in male disguise arrayed
To join the merry masquerade.

26

But having roused your interest
In fashion and the mode, you may,
As connoisseurs, expect me now
To describe Onegin's fine array.
But, look, you've put me to the test,
For, though description is my craft,
There are, alas, no words in Russian
For *pantaloons, frock-coat,* and *vest.*
Indeed, for as it is—I trust
You will forgive me for this sin—
My lines already are too gaudy
With words of foreign origin.
And yet I've always doted on
Our *Academic Lexicon.*[17]

27

But that is not my theme at present.
Let's hurry to the ball instead,
Where, headlong, in a cab Onegin
Flies fairly clattering ahead.
Along dark houses in a row,
Through silent avenues in slumber,
The carriage lamps before them cast
Their rainbow shadows on the snow.
But here's the gate, the noble mansion,
The tallow lights along the lanes,
And views of silhouetted forms
Across the curtained window-panes—
A profile moving to and fro
Of lovely maid or rakish beau.

28

Then past the butler, like an arrow
Our hero takes the marble stair,
And as he enters, in a hurry
He brushes back a lock of hair.
The lively ballroom buzzes loud
With dancers in the gay mazurka
While feebler sounds the orchestra
Amid the hubbub of the crowd.
Here, officers in clanking spurs;
Here pretty feet scud twinkling by
Pursued by envy in their flight
And many a captivated eye.
The fiddles crash; in bursts of sound
The gibes of jealous dames are drowned.

29

In my young days of joy and passion
On balls I madly used to dote:
No safer place for love affairs
And passing of a tender note.
But hearken every worthy spouse
And mark my warning! Here it goes,
An earnest word from one who knows,
To save the honor of your house.
You, too, mammas, should closely watch
Your pretty daughters at a dance.
Watch close with your lorgnettes! Or else—
May God forbid! I take this chance
Of warning you because, you know,
I've stopped my sinning long ago.

30

Ah, me! how many years I've wasted
In my pursuit of pleasure gay,
And yet, were morals not in question,
I'd feel the thrill of balls today.
I love mad youth; I do not mind
The whirling crowd, the mirth and glitter,
The artfulness of women's gowns,
Their pretty feet. You scarce will find
Throughout our country, I'm afraid,
Three pairs of shapely feet, all told.
Alas! I shall for long remember
Two little feet. Though sad and old
And grown too cold as I may seem
To you, they tease my waking dream.

31

What madness! Yet, who can forget
Their charm at any time or place?
Where now the summer field of bloom
They trampled in their dancing grace?
The East alone their kind has bred
And cherished them with tenderness
Unknown to northern lands of snow;
They learned in luxury to tread
On rugs voluptuous and soft.
How long since I for them forgot
The call of fame and men's applause,
My country, and an exile's lot!
But, like light footprints on the grass,
The joys of youth must also pass.

32

Diana's bosom, Flora's dimple
Are very charming; yet for me,
My friends, in charm far lovelier
The feet of our Terpsichore.
A token of a pleasure higher
Than any prize or gift of man,
Their gracefulness awakes in me
A swarm of wayward new desire.
I love them everywhere, my dears:
Beneath a table half concealed,
In winter by the open hearth,
In springtime on a grassy field,
In ballrooms on a polished floor,
Or on the rocks along the shore.

33

I well recall the waves at sea
Before a storm: I longed above
All else to rush with billows forth
And lie there at her feet, in love![18]
How much, together with the waves,
I yearned to fall before her feet,
For never in my young mad days,
When passion blazes and enslaves,
Grew I so sad with suffering,
And ardent with my fierce desire
To kiss the roses of her cheeks,
To kiss her breasts of languid fire!
No surging passion ever tore
My spirit with such pain before.

34

Another time I still remember
As in a dream: By her command,
I held for her the blessed stirrup
And felt her ankle in my hand.
How secretly I glowed again!
Once more her witchery and nearness
Inflamed that withered heart of mine
With sudden rapture, sudden pain! . . .
Enough! You've lauded haughty belles
Too long, and babbled with your lyre
Of charms not worthy of your songs
And tender feelings they inspire:
Believe, their looks and words are sweet,
Deceptive . . . as their little feet.

35

But where's Onegin? Half asleep,
He's driven home from ball to bed
When restless Petersburg is roused
To labor and its daily bread
By morning drums. Men come and go
And hawkers plod on bustling streets;
The cabmen lumber to their stands
And milkmaids haste in crunching snow.
The morning stirs with pleasant sounds;
The shutters open; chimneys spout
Their smoke aloft in columns blue;
The German baker is long about
His shop, trim in his cotton cap,
And answers to an early tap.

36

But, jaded from the ballroom turmoil,
From turning morning into night,
Our youth of elegance and pleasure
Sleeps blissfully in morning light.
Past midday, after his awaking,
He starts upon his merry rounds,
And tomorrows are as yesterdays,—
To sleep again when day is breaking.
But with these day-to-day enjoyments
Was Onegin happy, satisfied,
Delighted in the bloom of youth,
Content with triumphs in his pride?
Or did he in his feasting spend
Himself for an unworthy end?

37

'Tis true, Onegin soon grew cold
And dull, bored by society,
And scheming beauties only roused
Feelings of pain and *ennui*.
He took no pleasure in their vain
Affairs, in friendship and its claims;
He came to feel it was an outrage
To wash down always with champagne
Beefsteaks and Strasbourg pies, to pun
When his poor head began to ache—
To please a crowd of scatter-brains;
And though reputed as a rake,
In time he sickened and abhorred
The duel, pistol, and the sword.

38

Perhaps we'll diagnose in time
His malady and find its clues.
It's spleen in English for the present;
In Russian parlance—just the blues.[19]
But God be praised, he never tried
To shoot himself. Yet all the same
It mastered him by slow degrees,
And left him worn, unsatisfied;
And, like Childe Harold, sullenly
He drifted through each drawing-room,
Dismissing gossip, tender glances,
Or wanton sighs, or cards, with gloom.
He seemed indifferent and cold
And nothing moved him as of old.

'Twas you, O crotchety great dames,
Whom first Onegin left alone;
He found your haughty manners dull,
Inert in spiritual tone.
And though sometimes a lady may
Discourse on Say and Bentham,[20] still
Their trifling talk is as a rule
Unbearable. And then the way
Those creatures think themselves so clever,
So lofty-minded, calm, polite,
So pious, pure in their endeavors,
So circumspect, so strictly right,
And proof against all men! Their mien,
Their looks alone bring on the spleen.

43

You, too, O fairest belles and beauties,
Who wildly dash at night along
The avenues of Petersburg,
Eugene has left your mirthful throng.
To friends and gaiety he bade
Farewell. He shut himself indoors,
Refusing visitors, and, yawning,
Took up his pen and writing pad.
He tried a page. For steady work
Untrained, he soon gave up his plan,
And thus he never could become
A bumptious, brawling writing man,—
A person whom I can't condemn
Since, as you know, I'm one of them.

44

Once more the prey of idleness
And faint with spiritual dread,
He actively set out to make
His own what others thought and said.
He pondered in the company
Of books. He read, but read to no
Avail, because of humbug, lies,
Illusions, nonsense, flummery,—
Each mind enchained by dogmas all
Its own. Old things were stale, too old;
The new rehearsed the old by rote.
Like women's love, books left him cold.
He soon gave up their dusty brood
And left them on the shelves for good.

45

I, too, had come to shun mankind
And toss convention's yoke aside
When first we came to be good friends.
I liked his temper and self-pride,
The cool dissecting mind he had,
His clear inimitable way
Of seeing life with naked eyes.
I was resentful; he was sad.
We both felt wasted by the game
Of passion, wearied by the art
Of winning fame from early youth.
Our feelings ashen at the heart,
At best we both could but await
Men's hatred and the wrath of fate.

46

The man who lives and dares to think
Will scorn his fellow-men at last;
For him who feels, the troubled days
Arise like phantoms of the past.
All vain illusions and regret,
Repentance gnawing at the heart,
The serpent sting of memories
Long banished from the mind beget
A certain charm in conversation:
Onegin's sharp remarks at first
Disturbed me, but I later relished
His caustic arguments, his burst
Of passion, anger, savage wit,
His epigrams that aimed to hit.

47

How often on a summer evening
When midnight skies shone clear and bright
Above the Neva, lying still
And smiling in the mellow light
Without a moon or starlight gleaming,
We stood and talked of our romances.
We called to mind our love affairs
Of old, entranced by carefree dreaming,
And waited in the warm night air
In silence, deep in reverie!
Like prisoners who dream themselves
Transported to a greenwood, free,
We floated on the purer stream
Of blameless youth as in a dream.

48

Leaning against the granite wall,
Onegin in the midnight stood
And brooded long (as once a poet
Described in words the pensive mood.)[21]
No noise was heard in calm around
Except the shout of watchmen near,
Or carriage echoing along
A street far off with rattling sound.
At times upon the drowsy river
A lonely skiff moved lightly by;
A strain of song or shepherd's horn
Rang fainter with a dying sigh.
But best of all were Tasso's light
Sweet octaves to beguile the night.

49

O waters of the Adriatic!
O Brenta! I shall yet rejoice
When, roused again by inspiration,
I hear the magic of your voice
Dear to Apollo's progeny,
Exalted by the proudest lyre
Of Albion,[22] heartfelt as home
And bountiful as grace to me.
Once free, in golden Italy
I'll in a gondola rejoice
To hear within the witching hour
Of night a sweet Venetian voice,—
The tone of Petrarch's tender song
Revealed to me upon her tongue.

50

But when at last will come the hour,
My time of freedom, at my cry?
I wait fair winds upon the shore
And hail the passing sail.[23] Shall I
Fare never on the trackless way
At sea, in flight before the storms,
In battle with the raging billows?
High time I left behind this grey
And gloomy land, these hostile shores,
To find my glowing Afric sky,[24]
A sunlit shore beside a sea,
And there for doleful Russia sigh—
The land that knew my love, my pain,
Where buried deep my heart has lain.

51

Onegin would have been delighted
To visit many a foreign clime
With me, but through some circumstance
We parted for a lengthy time.
His father died. The creditors,
Who came in greedy companies
Prepared to justify their claims,
Crowded before Onegin's doors.
My friend, who hated litigation,
Accepting willingly his fate,
Without great forfeit to himself
For debts surrendered his estate.
Perhaps he guessed or saw ahead
His uncle's dying in his bed.

I wait fair winds upon the shore
And hail the passing sail.

52

Indeed, he soon received a letter
In which the bailiff wrote to tell
Him that his uncle then was dying
And wished to bid his heir farewell.
Without delay Onegin sped
By swiftest post, though bored about
The journey and the interview,
To reach in time his uncle's bed.
He knew the task would sorely try him,
For he would have to lie—the shame—
For the inheritance (with which
The novel opened). When he came,
His uncle's body lay in state,
A tribute due our earthly fate.

53

He found, from all the country round,
A host of friends and enemies
Had swarmed from far to pay their calls
And to enjoy the obsequies.
The dead was duly buried. Priest
And guests refreshed themselves devoutly
At tables heaped with food and drink,
Then gravely rose and left the feast.
Behold Onegin, lord of streams
And forests, fields and meadow lands,
A spendthrift liver who abhorred
The steady work of human hands,
Yet glad to own he understood
A change of life might do him good.

54

For two full days he was delighted
To wander over field and hill,
To feel the coolness of the groves
And hear the babbling of the rill.
But by the third he had no more
Desire to seek the grove, or field,
Or rill; the country walks and rides
Began to pall, and then, to bore.
And though it had no garish streets
Or lofty palaces to view,
Or clubs and balls, or cards and verses,
The spleen was in the country too
That like a shadow dogged his life,
Like a devoted loving wife.

55

For me, I like a life of quiet,
And village silence pleases me:
In solitude my lyric song
Rings clear and I am fancy-free.
I like to wander by the lake
At leisure, satisfied, at peace,
With *far niente* as my guide
In life. Each morning I awake
To freedom and sweet ease again;
I seldom read; I sleep, I rest,
And do not brood on worldly fame.
I now recall I always blessed
Those tranquil years unknown to praise,
My best, my happiest of days.

I like to wander by the lake
At leisure, satisfied, at peace

56

And there I give my heart's devotion
To flowers, love, to idleness,
And fields! I'm not like my Onegin,
A difference I wish to stress,
Lest a malicious clever mind,
Some reader or some editor
Who dotes on shrewd insinuations
Might sometime say that he could find
My features in Onegin's portrait,
That I, unblushing, glorified
Myself in this poetic novel,
Like Byron, bard of lofty pride—
As though no poet had been known
To paint a likeness not his own.[25]

57

But I'll admit all poets lose
Themselves in glowing reverie.
I, too, have dreamed of women fair
Whom long my soul in secrecy
Beheld in loveliness portrayed,
Whose vision later I made live
In verse. And thus, light-heartedly,
I've praised in song the mountain maid,
My own ideal, and captive women
Along the beaches of Salghír.[26]
"But who is now your inspiration?"
This question, friends, I often hear;
"To whom among the jealous throng
Do you now dedicate your song?

58

"Whose eyes, that stir your inspiration,
With joy and tenderness repay
The music of your pensive lays?
What goddess moves your heart today?"
I swear I call no goddess mine!
I've suffered in my time too long
The senseless pangs of burning love.
Happy the man who can combine
Poetic work with love and thus
Enhance its sacred ecstasy,
Who seeks, like Petrarch, consolation
For love's distress and misery
And wins perchance some good repute.
But I, in love, am dull and mute.

59

But love has gone. The Muse appears
And, with a mind serene again,
I feel I'm free to fuse my thoughts
And fancies in one magic strain.
I write,—my heart feels quieted.
Lost in my work, I do not trace
Beside my rough unfinished stanzas
Some shapely foot or lovely head;
My heart is ash, and though I'm sad,
I have no tears, despite my grief.
Soon, soon I think I shall forget
The storms that shook me like a leaf,
And then—why then I'll write a song
In five-and-twenty cantos long.

My plan is made, my hero named,
And thus my work is well begun;
Meanwhile, I'm even pleased to find
I have completed Chapter One.
I've scrutinized each page anew,
And, though aware of many blunders,
I do not wish to change a line.
Let censorship collect its due.
Let greedy critics rend asunder
My work of thought and dedication!
And so make haste to face the world,
My youngest born, my new creation,
And earn the tribute paid to fame:
Men's idle talk, abuse, and blame.

Chapter Two

O rus!
Horace
O Russia!

I

The manor where Onegin fretted
Was a delightful rural spot;
There friends of simple tastes enjoyed
Their lives, contented with their lot.
The manor house, from wind and storm
Deep-sheltered by a wooded hill,
Was set beside a stream. Beyond,
Upon a plain in sunlight warm
Lay peasant villages near fields
Of golden grain and meadows gay
With flowers, where herds at pasture roved.
There vast, neglected gardens lay
And contemplative dryads made
Their refuge in the dark green shade.

2

This stately country home was built
As ancient houses used to be
For solid comfort, prized by men
Of taste and true nobility.
The lofty halls and rooms were fair
With portraits of the royal house,
High stoves of polished colored tiles,
And damask cloth on couch and chair.
All this is said to be old-fashioned
And out of date, I know not why,
Although I'm positive this matter
Was far too trivial to try
Onegin, bored alike by past
And modern fashions first or last.

3

He chose the room his uncle lived in
For forty years without a break,
Scolded his housekeeper, killed flies,
Or near the window lay awake.
The room was simple: oaken floors,
Two cupboards, chairs, a downy sofa,
And a table still without a spot
Of ink. Behind the cupboard doors
Onegin found a row of wines,
Liqueurs, clay jars of applejack,
A yellowed ledger in one corner,
An Eighteen-Eight worn almanac.
His uncle never cared to look
In any other kind of book.

4

Alone on his estate, Onegin,
To pass the time, began to dream
Of rural welfare and reform
By setting up a new regime.
He soon decided to abate
The burden of coercive labor
And introduce a light quit-rent.[1]
The peasants blessed their happy fate.
Then sullenly a thrifty neighbor
Declared that novelty appeared
A fad, a dreadful wrong; others
Made sport of it, or glumly sneered.
Yet all agreed one point was clear—
He was quite dangerous and queer.

5

At first his neighbors came to call;
But when they found, to their dismay,
He often had his stallion ready
At the back porch, to dash away
Whenever he became aware
Of gentry carts upon the highway,
They were offended and declared
His rudeness was too much to bear:
"Onegin's crazy, a *formasón*,[2]
A boorish chap—you understand!
He drinks red wine in tumblers only
And does not kiss a lady's hand;
He won't say *Ma'am*, just *yes* or *no*."
Their estimates of him were low.

6

At that same time another squire
Returned to live on his estate,
Whose ways excited disapproval
And neighbors' censure quite as great.
Vladimir Lensky was his name.
A handsome youth of manly bearing,
A Kantian devotee and poet,
Direct from Göttingen he came.[3]
He brought with him some vague ideals
In fashion then in Germany,
A mind eccentric, ardent, dreaming
An age of widespread liberty,
Impassioned words of lofty grace
And jet black locks about his face.

7

One yet unspotted by the world's
Corruption and unfaithfulness,
His soul was set aglow by friendship
Or by a woman's tenderness.
Thus, inexperienced and kind,
He lived with his acquired illusions,
By faith and hopes untried in life,
Enchanted in his heart and mind;
With dreams and sweet imagination
He quieted each stirring doubt,
And earthly life appeared to him
A mystery past finding out.
He struggled, seeking to divine
The marvel of the world's design.

8

He felt a kindred soul was destined
To be united with his own,
And that it waited, sorrowing,
Day after day for him alone;
He trusted loyal friends would come
To fight for him in honor's name,
That they would crush the enemy
And slanderer. He felt that some
Great spirits are by Fate elected
A dedicated noble race
That will in everlasting time
Bring men into a world of grace,
And that a glory yet to be
Will shine in our eternity.

9

He early knew just indignation;
Compassion for the common good
And love of glory long had stirred
With pity and sweet pain his mood.
He wandered, worshipping the lyre,
And, at the altar flame of Goethe
And Schiller, his exalted spirit
Was kindled by their lyric fire.
He never in his verse dishonored
The Muses by his lofty art,
But proudly in his songs enshrined
The noblest promptings of his heart,
A soul of virgin reverie,
A charm of grave simplicity.

10

The slave of love, he sang its praises
In stanzas like a ray of light,
As artless as a maiden's fancy
Or infant's dream, or as the night
Of quiet silver moonlight shining
Upon a lover's tender sighs.
He sang of spheres mysterious,
Of parting, sorrow, and repining;
He sang of something vague, afar,
Free lands and seas, and roses blowing
Where long, in silence and in joy,
His tears of happiness were flowing;
Though scarce eighteen, he sang, in brief,
His life was in the yellow leaf.

11

None but Onegin could appraise
His nature in that rural waste,
For Lensky found the country gentry
Too uninspiring for his taste.
He fled their noisy conversations:
Their dinners and their rounds of pleasure,
Their solemn talk of crops and brandies,
Of stables, kennels, and relations,
Seemed unendurably too dull,
Completely lacking in true wit
And feeling, in the art of living,
In grace or common benefit;
But duller yet the daily chaff
And gossip of the fairer half.

12

A rich and handsome youth, our Lensky
Was welcomed as a bachelor
By neighbors with unmarried daughters,
For such the way of rustic lore.
For him, one rich and German-bred,
Their talk would oft deplore the lone,
Poor single life and boast the joys
Of men and women matched and wed.
And oft their harmless conversation
At teas, in honor of their guest,
Would end by begging Dúnya, please
To sing a nice romance, her best.
And, oh, good Lord! to hear her bleat
"Come to my golden chamber, Sweet!"[4]

And, oh, good Lord! to hear her bleat
"Come to my golden chamber, Sweet!"

13

But Lensky certainly was not
Concerned with marriage bonds—not yet;
He longed instead to meet and know
Onegin well. At last they met.
Like rock and wave, like ice and flame,
Like prose and poetry, the two
Were so diverse in character,
They bored each other. All the same
They met as neighbors do, and soon
Their liking grew for one another.
They met on daily rides, drew closer
Each day as brother does to brother.
Thus friends are made (I'm guilty too)
For want of something else to do.

14

But even that poor sort of friendship
Appears, like prejudice, outgrown,
Because we rate all men as nothing
And count ourselves as ends alone;
We look on all mankind as tools—
The million-legged hosts of people
Used by Napoleons, who leave
Pure sentiment to clowns and fools.
More tolerant, more kind than most,
Onegin was; although he knew
The world too well and scorned mankind,
He could be gentle, could be true,
Could value feelings in a friend
And be unselfish to the end.

15

He listened to young Lensky, smiling.
The poet's heated conversation,
His immature and hasty thinking,
His fiery words of inspiration,
Amused him by their novelty.
He struggled not to interpose
A scornful note or mocking word,
And thought: "His youthful ecstasy
Will slowly wear itself away
And, in the course of time, he'll face
Reality, but meanwhile let
Him think the world's a perfect place.
I'll overlook the fever sweet,
His frenzy, his poetic heat."

16

And thus, in frequent conversations
And long debates, they freely spoke
Their minds on ancient sovereign rights,
The fruits of science and the yoke
Of custom, public wrong and good.
They talked of human destiny
And mysteries beyond the grave,
Then state affairs, and brotherhood.
Vladimir Lensky in the heat
Of argument would oft rehearse
Some lines of Russian poetry,
But, puzzled by the glowing verse,
Onegin smiled indulgently,
Despite their ambiguity.

17

Still oftener the tender passion
Engaged these would-be eremites.
Onegin, freed from its dominion,
Conversed of love and its delights
With sighs of deep, constrained regret.
Blessed the man who'd known their fervor
But had escaped their pangs at last;
Twice blessed he who had not let
One love enslave his mind, who'd cooled
His blood with parting, or disdained
All hate; who, bored, had stayed with wife
And friends by jealousy unstained,
Who guarded his inheritance
And shunned the crafty games of chance.

18

When, wise in years, we seek at last
The refuge of tranquility;
When flaming loves begin to fade
With all their wayward ecstasy,
And sequels of late wilfulness
Are truly tamed by self-restraint;
When in our sorrow we reflect
What stupid habits we confess
Were ours,—we find our joy in tales
Of love a stranger has to tell.
Thus a grizzled veteran delights
To hear, in his secluded cell,
Tall stories told by young hussars
About their battles and their scars.

19

Besides, impassioned youth can scarce
Its inner sentiments of grief
Or love conceal, but babbles all
Its joys and fears—to find relief.
Onegin with a grave expression,
Himself a veteran from his own
Affairs of passion, heard the poet
Rejoice to make a free confession.
In every word of confidence
Revealed, proceeding from the heart,
Onegin read the youth's romance
Without real trying on his part,—
A tale of love forever true
Since time began, but never new.

20

Ah, Lensky loved as people love
No longer in our world of late,
As only wild poetic souls
Are doomed to love: Inviolate,
Forever one his inspiration,
His one and constant dream of life,
His one and ever-present sorrow!
And never years of separation,
Nor love of books, nor solitude,
Nor hours devoted to the arts,
Nor gay companionship with friends,
Nor charming scenes in foreign parts,
Could make him doubt his soul's desire,
Still glowing with its virgin fire.

21

When but a lad, he'd been enraptured
By little Olga; as a boy
He shared in all dear innocence
Her childish sports and childish joy.
In their secluded bowers, at play,
They shared their games, the while their parents,
As friends and long familiar neighbors,
Planned smilingly the marriage day.
In peaceful solitary glades
And rural sweetness, Olga grew
Beneath her parents' watchful eyes
As lilies of the valley do
In tallest grass, in secrecy,
Unknown to butterfly or bee.

22

Fair Olga was the first to stir
His dreaming soul when they were young
Together, and thoughts of Olga first
Inspired his virgin lyric song.
Farewell to childhood days of light!
For now he loved the wildwood gloom,
The silence and the solitude,
The moon and stars, the lonely night.
But most he loved the brooding moon,
The lamp within the evening shining,
To which in walks apart we vow
Our grief and sighs in secret pining,—
The moon now deemed a substitute
For street-lamps when we are afoot.

23

Demure and gentle, simple-hearted
As Lensky's soul unstained by guile,
Sweet as a kiss of lovers sworn
And tender as the waking smile
Of dawn, with roses in her face,
With eyes of azure, flaxen hair,
His Olga was in voice and motion
A dream of loveliness and grace. . . .
Dear reader, you can find her portrait
In many novels of our day;
There was a time I deemed it sweet.
I'm fed up now! And, by the way,
Her elder sister, in her turn,
Must have her share of my concern.

24

Tatyána was her sister's name.[5]
We are the first, yet not by chance,
To glorify with a common name
The heroine of a new romance.
Why not? It has a pleasant sound,
Although I know our memories
Of ancient ways and servants' halls
Inevitably cling around
That name. Let's grant we now are poor
In grace and show but little taste
In names—especially in verse;
Our culture is a thing abased,
Endowing us as heretofore
With affectation—nothing more.

25

Her name, Tatyána. But, not hers,
Alas, her sister's pretty face,
Her sweet attractiveness of mien,
Her rosy loveliness and grace.
As timid as a forest fawn,
She moved in silence and in sadness,
And even among her own she seemed
Estranged, within herself withdrawn.
She never learned to please her parents
By cuddling in a childlike way,
And far too shy with other children
She did not care to romp and play,
But would beside the window brood
For hours alone in solitude.

26

She was from infancy a child
Of reverie, the placid stream
Of rural ease and leisure wreathed
With shining fancies of her dream.
Her tender fingers never traced
A careful seam; she never lingered
Above a frame, embroidering
In silk the linen to her taste.
A child at play with dolls that mind
Her warning to be good, prepares
Herself unwittingly for all
Proprieties and daily cares
When, like mamma in accents grave,
She warns her dollies to behave.

27

But Tanya always turned away
From dolls, and never had been known
To babble to a doll the talk
Of grownup folks. She walked alone
Among the romping children at
Their games. Instead, her heart was thrilled
By tales of horror told at night
By housemaids meeting for a chat.
When nanny gathered Olga's playmates
About her on the lawn to roam
And play their games of barley-brake,
Poor Tanya stayed alone at home,
Bored by the merriment and noise
Of giddy girls and shouting boys.

28

Upon her balcony, at dawn,
Tatyána loved to greet the day
And watch the galaxies of stars
On pale horizons fade away
Where heaven's rim grew gently clear,
Where breezes blew before the rise
Of morning slowly wakening.
In winter, when the hemisphere
Was shrouded in the realm of night,
And, lingering, the Orient
Beneath the cold and misty moon
Lay dozing late in languishment,
Awaking promptly from her rest,
By candle-light she rose and dressed.

29

She took to novels from the first,
And all her days she lived aglow
With stories of conceit and fancy
By Richardson and by Rousseau.
Her father never cared to look
At novels but that kindly man,
Left long ago behind the times,
Could see no mischief in a book;
He thought the printed page a waste
Of time, and, having rarely read,
He little cared what secret novel
His child was reading late in bed.
As for his wife, she doted on
The works of Samuel Richardson.

30

She worshipped Richardson but not
Because she'd read him, not because
She really thought that Grandison
A better man than Lovelace was,
But she had only heard Aline,
Her Moscow cousin, speak with praise
About those two romantic figures.
As for herself, at seventeen,
Her hand was plighted by her parents,
Before she knew her mind, to him
She later married, though she sighed
For one who pleased her girlish whim;
That Grandison was great at cards,
A fop, a sergeant of the Guards.

31

Like his, her dress was elegant,
Becoming to her, and in mode;
But still, without her free consent,
Her hand in wedlock was bestowed.
Her husband acted sensibly
And took her, to divert her grief,
At once to his ancestral seat
Far in the country wilds, where she
With God knows whom about her grieved
And wept, bewailed her fate, and meant
To leave, but turned to household duties,
Grew reconciled, and then content.
Praise God for habit then and bless
His gift in lieu of happiness.

32

Sweet habit thus beguiled her sorrow
As nothing else could have allayed
Her grief, till full relief appeared
From one discovery she'd made:
Between her duties and her leisure
She gained the insight and the craft
To run the business of the household
And rule her husband at her pleasure.
She managed fields, shaved peasant locks,[6]
And kept accounts and entry-books.
She steamed herself on Saturdays,
And pickled mushrooms with her cooks.
She chose to beat the maids, reprieve,
And never by her husband's leave.

33

Time was she wrote an album verse
In blood,[7] her loves and feelings keen;
She spoke a sing-song drawl and called
Praskóvya by the name Pauline.
Time was she sounded through her nose
Our Russian *n*'s in throaty French,
And laced her corsets very tight.
A spouse, she dropped her foreign pose:
Those albums, sentimental verses,
Her corsets, dear princess Pauline,
Were all forgotten; she said Akúlka
Like other folks and not Celine;
She fashioned, too, by native lore,
The wadded robe and cap she wore.

34

Her husband loved her ever dearly
And let her manage house and farm
With perfect trust; he spent his days
In dressing gown and feared no harm.
And thus his placid years rolled by
Without a care. Sometimes at dusk
Old neighbors round about dropped in
Informally,—to gossip, sigh,
Or chat at once about some graver
Matter, to laugh, to play a game
Or two at cards, while Olga served
Them tea, till time for supper came;
And thus the end of one more day,
Before the guests would drive away.

35

They treasured in their peaceful life
The dear old ways of other days:
When Shrovetide came, they served their guests
Fat pancakes in old country ways;
They made confession twice a year;
They loved the ancient Christmas carols,
The swings, the dance of choral rings.
At Whitsuntide, when people near
Them yawned throughout the morning mass,
In deep humility and prayer
They shed some tears on buttercups.[8]
Their *kvass* was plentiful as air;
They served at dinners of their best,
By rank and order, every guest.

36

And so they lived, grew old together.
A day arrived, when ill and hoary,
The husband passed beyond the tomb,
And thus received his crown of glory.
He passed into eternity
At noon, mourned by his wife and children,
By neighbors and by friends, as few
Are mourned, with deep sincerity.
He was a master kind and plain,
Unstained by cunning or caprice.
His epitaph was graved in stone:
An humble sinner, now at peace,
God's servitor and brigadier,
Dimitry Larin, sleepeth here.

Back home in his ancestral halls,
Vladimir Lensky visited
His neighbor's tomb and there he mourned
Above the ashes of the dead;
Then, sighing, said dejectedly:
"*Poor Yorick*!⁹ He was wonderful.
He used to hold me in his arms,
And often in my infancy
I played with his Ochákov medals.
I still can hear him say he gave
Me Olga, hoped to see us wed."
And, sorrowing beside the grave,
Young Lensky in sad memory
Composed a mournful elegy.

38

There, too, in tears, he bowed above
His father's and his mother's dust,
And wept at memories he loved. . . .
Alas! that generations must
Upon the furrowed fields of being
Spring up and droop, age after age
Arise and bloom, then die again
By a will supreme beyond our seeing.
And ever thus our human race
Must wax and surge, a seething mass,
And crowd its forebears to their graves.
And thus we too, we too shall pass.[10]
In time our children, even so,
Will crowd us out, and we must go.

39

But meanwhile drink your fill of life,
As fragile as it is, my friends!
I know its emptiness too well
And care but little how it ends.
I am deceived by no illusion;
Yet all my hopes of greater fame
Awaiting me still agitate
My heart sometimes with new confusion:
I live nor write for praise, but fear
To die unknown in fame and story.
I'd rather win a little place
For my sad name, some share of glory,
One note,—one line of poetry,
That, like a friend, shall speak for me.

A simple fellow may some day
Point to my portrait and declare:
"He was a poet, a man of scope!"

40

Perhaps my lines a stranger's heart
May move; perhaps, by luck or fate,
At last dark Lethe will not swallow
The stanzas I today create.
Perhaps (what overweening hope!)
A simple fellow may some day
Point to my portrait and declare:
"He was a poet, a man of scope!"
O lover of the peaceful Muses,
Receive my thanks and salutation,—
O dearest friend, whose memory
Will shrine my fugitive creation,
Whose hand of grace may yet caress
An old man's bays with tenderness!

Chapter Three

Elle était fille, elle était amoureuse.

Malfilâtre

I

"Where are you off to? Oh, you poets!"
"Goodbye, Onegin, I must go."
"I'm not detaining you, but where
Do you spend your time I'd like to know?"
"At the Larins'." "I say, that's queer!
I'm sure you find it rather boring
To kill your evenings at their place."
"No, not at all, my friend!" "I fear
I may misjudge you, yet I'll guess
Your reasons, and I think I'm right:
A plain old Russian family
Where guests are welcomed with delight,
With tea, preserves, and endless prattle
About the weather, flax, and cattle."

2

"I do not see what's wrong with that."
"Why, boredom, man! It's pretty clear."
"What if I hate your modern ways,
And like their homelike atmosphere
Where I . . ." "Another pastoral!
Good Lord, enough! You're really going?
I'm sorry. Listen, I'd be pleased
Indeed to meet sometime your—well,
Your Phyllis, whom you idolize,
The charming girl to whom you owe
Your poems, dreams, *et cetera.*
Come, introduce me!" "Jesting?" "No!"
"I'm glad." "But when?" "Tonight! You'll see,
They'll gladly have us—you and me."

3

"Let's go!"
         And fast the two rode off.
The ladies met them graciously
At home with plain, solicitous,
Old-fashioned hospitality,
With simple rites made popular
By custom: saucers of preserves
And cranberry water set upon
An oilcloth'd table, in a jar.[1]

. . . .
. . . .
. . . .
. . . .
. . . .

4

Then quickly by the shortest road
They hurried homeward on their way.
Now let us overhear by stealth
Just what our heroes had to say.
"What now, Onegin, yawning still?"
"From habit." "Yet you seem somehow
More bored than usual." "No. Look here,
The sun's gone down beyond that hill.
Hey, hurry, hurry home, Andryúshka!
What dreary countryside! I say,
Your Larina is plain and sweet,
A nice old lady. By the way,
Their treat of jam and cranberry,
I fear, will disagree with me.

5

"But tell me, which is their Tatyána?"
"The one who with an absent air,
And melancholy, like Svetlána,[2]
Came in and took the window chair."
"You love the younger, I infer?"
"Well?" "I would choose the other girl
Were I a poet like yourself.
Young Olga has no soul in her;
I mean her face is round and rosy
Much like Van Dyck's *Madonna*. Why,
She seems like that insipid moon
Aloft in that insipid sky."
Poor Lensky answered drily, stirred
At heart, then said not one more word.

6

Meantime Onegin's sudden visit
At Larins' as their evening guest
Made everywhere a great impression
And roused the neighbors' interest.
"He courts Tatyána" ran the rumor,
And guess came quickly after guess.
Some gossiped, mingling talk with spite,
Some jested fairly in good humor,
Some even set the wedding date
And some for certain were assured
The long delay was all about
New-fashioned rings to be procured.
Young Lensky's matrimonial fate
They said was now beyond debate.

7

Tatyána heard their gossip, vexed
In spirit; yet her heart would fill
With strange, ineffable elation
And secret joy against her will.
A dream was born, enravishing
Her being; now her time had come—
She was in love. Thus grows a seed
When quickened by the sun of spring.
Long since, her young imagination,
Aglow with yearning tenderness,
Had hungered for this fateful food;
Long since, in secret languidness
She'd yearned, imprisoned in her gloom.
Her soul had waited—but for whom?

8

The hour had come. Her spirit knew;
She whispered to herself: "Tis he!"
Always, in fevered dream or waking,
The same bright vision constantly
Before her gaze; the air around
Proclaims his presence; everywhere
His image shines with magic power.
How wearisome to her the sound
Of kindly words at home, the servants'
Solicitude and care! She pays
No heed to any guests; she hates
Their dallying and trifling ways,
Each unexpected friendly call
Or lingering at evenfall.

9

With what new eagerness again
She reads each dear romance, and how
Intense and sweet the fascination
Of their seductive pages now!
Her fancy, quickened by the spell
Of inspiration, gives new life
To the lover of Julie Wolmar,
To de Linar, Malek-Adhel,
Young Werther, brave in suffering,
And that unrivaled paragon
Who bores us dreadfully today,
That noblest, fairest Grandison.[3]
In every form, in every face
She sees Onegin's form and grace.

For days in her imagination
Julie, Clarissa, or Delphine,[4]
She wandered in the quiet groves,
Making herself the heroine
Of each romance revealed by art.
She found in every circumstance
Her meditated secret dream,
The passion of her brimful heart;
Another's grief became her sorrow,
Another's ecstasy, her own;
And to herself she spoke the words
Of love she meant for him alone. . . .
But the hero she was dreaming on
For certain was no Grandison.

Time was a glowing author tuned
His style to a majestic key
And made his hero an example
Of excellence and gallantry.
Each hero was a man whose mind
And handsome face appeared endowed
With every gift of grace and feeling.
Though hounded, scorned among mankind,
Through genuine self-sacrifice,
His heart with purest passion glowing,
The hero triumphed at the last
In the concluding chapter, showing
That vice is punished and abhorred,
That virtue wins its just reward.

12

But human minds are now befogged;
What's more, we're bored by moral tales;
In novels even vice is pleasant
When it triumphantly prevails.
The British tales and fables now
Disturb our adolescent girls:
New idols win their adoration—
The Vampire of the pensive brow,
The gloomy vagabond Melmoth,
The Wandering Jew, the bold Corsair,
Or the mysterious Sbogar.[5]
Lord Byron's whimsical despair
Endowed men's hopeless egotism
With gloomy, sad romanticism.

13

But why this nonsense, to what end,
My friends? Perhaps by fate's decree
I shall yet cease to be the poet;
Another demon ruling me,
I shall defy Apollo's rage
In my descent to lowly prose.
A novel of old-fashioned times
Will then beguile my glad ripe age;
No secret agonies of crime
Will I in stories ruthlessly
Reveal, but draw instead the scenes
Of Russian domesticity.
The charm of youth and lovers' dreams,
And old-time ways shall be my themes.

14

I will rehearse the simple lives
Of dad and grandad in my book:
Their children's secret trysts beneath
The linden dreaming by the brook;
The pangs of jealousy, the dread
Of parting, tears of sweet avowal.
At times I'll set them quarreling,
But in the end I'll have them wed.
I will recapture then their words
Of passion, words of love and sweet
Desire that trippingly my lips
Had spoken at my darling's feet—
The words I used when I was young,
Sweet words no longer on my tongue.

15

Tatyána, dear Tatyána, I weep
My tears for you; all desolate
You have unto a modish tyrant
Resigned the keeping of your fate.
It is your hour of doom. But first,
Bewildered, blinded by your hope,
What dreams of happiness are yours!
What languor cool unto your thirst
To drain the magic vial of deep
Desire, to live in phantasy
By dreaming of the happy tryst
In every nook and bower you see!
At every turn, in every place,
Before you looms your tempter's face.

16

With love and anguish in her heart
Tatyána in the garden strays.
Too faint with languor and with grief,
She stops in weariness, her gaze
Upon the path, and deeply sighs.
The sudden hues of tender feeling
Suffuse her feverish pale cheeks
And blind with flashing light her eyes.
Night comes with stars. Aloft, the moon
Goes slowly on her watchful rounds;
The nightingale's repeated song
Among the still, dark trees resounds.
Wakeful, Tatyána lies and low
She whispers to her nurse her woe.

17

"It's stuffy, nurse, I cannot sleep;
Open the window. Please, stay here."
"What ails you, Tanya?" "Oh, I'm sad,
So sad! Tell me a story, dear."
"What story, Tanya? I used to know
So many, many olden stories
Of knights and maids and evil spirits;
Some ballads, too, of long ago
I knew right well by heart. But now
My mind is muddled, in a haze.
And I've forgotten what I knew
For good." "Tell me about the days
When you were young. In days long gone
Were you in love with anyone?"

18

"Hush, Tanya, hush! We never dared
To speak of courtship openly:
For all such talk my mother-in-law
Would well have been the death of me."
"How did you marry then?" "I mean
To say, my child, God willed it so.
Not quite as old as I was Ványa,
And I was going on fourteen.
For near two weeks the matchmaker
Kept urging on the marriage rite.
The day my father gave his blessing
I wept in bitterness and fright.
They loosed my braids; then I was led
In fear to church and thus was wed.

19

And so I came to be with strangers. . . .
But you're not listening, my pet."
"O nanny, nanny dear! I feel
So broken-hearted and upset,
So down at heart that I could weep!"
"My darling child, you must be ill.
I'll sprinkle you with holy water.
May God in his great mercy keep
And comfort you! You're burning hot;
You really have a fever." "No! . . .
I'm well. I am . . . you know . . . in love."
"May God be with you!" Bending low,
She prayed beside poor Tanya's bed
And signed the cross above her head.

20

"I am in love." Tatyána whispered
Her sad complaint. "My child, my dove!
You're ill, you're not at all yourself
Tonight." "No, no! . . . I am in love."
The moon shone silver in the air
With languid splendor in the room
Upon Tatyána's pallid shoulders,
Upon her loosened braids of hair,
Her trembling tears, and on the footstool
Beside the bed where sat her nurse,
Wrapped in her robe, with a kerchief
Around her head. The universe
Lay still within the magic night,
Enchanted by the pale moonlight.

21

Tatyána's thought in her ecstasy
On far strange moonlit air was blown.
Then quickly her decision came,
The Lord knows how. "Leave me alone,
My darling. Yes, I shall be soon
In bed. But first move up this table
Closer. I'll have my pen and paper."
Alone, in silence deep. The moon
Shone brighter. Far into the night
Tatyána wrote without pretense
In words unstudied and impulsive
Her maiden love and innocence.
Her letter's done. Dear child, reply,
What have you dared to write, and why?

22

I've known imperious great ladies
As winter cold, as pure as ice,
Implacable, inscrutable,
Not to be bribed at any price.
I've marveled at their worth inbred,
Their virtues, loftiness and pride,
But I confess I fled their presence
For on their foreheads I had read
The flaming words of Hell inscribed:
'Abandon hope who enter here.'
Their glances drove away compassion
And filled the human heart with fear.
Perhaps upon the Neva shore
Such ladies you have known before.

23

As one among the faithful suitors
I've known some freakish ladies who
Remained unmoved by lovers' sighs,
Self-centered, inwardly untrue.
And I have found to my surprise
How by the art of stern demeanor
They scared shy love away. Yet they
Contrived to lure their wonted prize
At least with covert sympathy,
At least with accents tender, kind,
With seeming feeling for their victim,
Until the youth, as ever blind
And ever foolish, would pursue
The charming conqueror anew.

24

Why censure then Tatyána's action?
Because in dear simplicity,
Believing in her chosen dream,
She practiced no duplicity?
Because her passion lacked fine art,
And, faithful to her inner longing
By grace of Heaven granted her,
She yielded to her dreaming heart?
Because her life was richly dowered
With passionate imagination,
With gifts of mind and will, a heart
Of tenderness and exultation?
And shall we no forgiveness find
For impulses thus rash and blind?

25

No flirt's unfeeling calculation,
Tatyána's love was deep and true.
In self-surrender to her fancy
She loved as charming children do.
She did not judge that some delay
Might soon enhance the price of love
And lure him to her nets; that she
Must flatter him at first, then play
A game of hope and indecision,
Or fan the flame of jealousy,
Bewildering his heart at will,
Lest, jaded with satiety,
The crafty bondman might essay
To break his chains and slip away.

26

I now foresee one more delay:
To vindicate my work and name,
I must translate Tatyána's letter
Or bring my country into shame.
She never learned her way too well
In Russian forms of speech, nor read
The books and journals that we publish,
Nor learned correctly how to spell,
And hence she wrote, of course, in French.
Our ladies, I am free to say,
Do not profess their sentiments
In Russian, in our native way,
And seem unable to compose
A line in simple Russian prose.

27

We should compel them, so I'm told,
To study Russian. What a crime
To suffer them to skim with profit
Our *Moral Mentor* at any time![6]
O poets, I appeal to you,
Do bear me out! Of those fair creatures
For whom in secret you were wont
To write your verse and sing of rue
And joy, as consecrated men,—
I ask, was not their Russian rated
Laborious and lame, in grammar
Too often sweetly mutilated,
While on their lips the alien speech
Seemed natural and fair for each?

God grant I never meet a lady
Academician at a ball,
Or greet a literary scholar
In lacy cap and silken shawl!

81

28

God grant I never meet a lady
Academician at a ball,
Or greet a literary scholar
In lacy cap and silken shawl![7]
Like rosy lips that never smile,
The sound of Russian speech correct
By rules of grammar I dislike.
Perhaps, in spite of me, meanwhile
The fair of younger generations,
As all reviews entreat and teach,
Will learn grammatical conceits
And meters for their common speech.
But as for me, unto the last
I will be faithful to our past.

29

Their faulty speech and careless prattle,
Their phrasing often wrong or bold
Still freshly agitate my heart
With lasting pleasure as of old.
I cannot change my mind, I fear.
For me, as our little sins of youth,
As Bogdanóvich's sweet verse,[8]
I hold their gallicisms dear.
Enough! I must translate the letter
Of my beloved heroine.
I gave my word. By God, I wish
I might beg off. But let's begin.
I wish that Parny's[9] tender phrase
Were still the fashion nowadays!

30

O bard of feasts[10] and languid sorrow,
If you were here with me, my guest,
I would be bold, dear friend of mine,
To make an indiscreet request,—
To take this maiden's passionate
But foreign lines and fashion them
In magic cadence of your art.
Where do you tarry? Come, translate
Her letter, for I yield my right
With reverence to you alone. . . .
Indifferent at heart to praise,
In Finland's gloom of granite stone
He wanders in his banishment,
And cannot heed my sad lament.

31

Tatyána's letter lies before me;
I guard it like a sacred thing.
I read it word by word, entranced,
But sad with secret pondering.
Who gave her power to impart
In words of overflowing feeling
Her tenderness, her sweet confusion,
The rapture of a loving heart,
So baneful in its fascination?
I cannot comprehend the whole
Of her. But here's at best my poor
Pale copy of a living soul,
As poor as *Freischütz*[11] rendered by
A pupil still untrained and shy.

Tatyána to Onegin

I write to you. Could I do more,
Or dare another word to say
In self-defense? I know you may
Now scorn me fully, or ignore.
But if you feel you have for me
One drop of pity, then I pray
You won't despise me secretly.
I thought I would not say a word
At first. Believe, you would have heard
No whisper of my secret shame
Had I some hope, a slender claim
That I might see you once a week
At home, look for a word of greeting,
Then listen gladly when you speak,
Or answer you with glance or phrase,—
To think and think for nights and days,
Then wait until another meeting.
But you're unsociable, they say,

And bored by country life. We do
Not shine at home in any way
But we were glad to welcome you.

What made you ever come to see
Us here? In this forgotten place
I never should have met you face
To face and known the misery
I feel. I might have found the grace
To curb the tumult of my life.
I might have loved (who knows) another,
And might have proved a blameless wife,
A dutiful, devoted mother.

No, no! That could not really be!
For yours alone this heart of mine!
By a higher Will my destiny
Was sealed, by a decree divine:
The meaning of my life,—to plight
Undying faith alone to you.
God led your steps to me—I knew
It well—to be my kindly light.
You came in dreams to me, so near
I knew your features, always dear;
I languished in your wondrous gaze;
I heard your voice on many days
Remembered long,—it was to me
At once so real. You came, I knew!
Confused with cold and fire I grew,
And all my soul cried, 'It is he!'
Was it not you who evermore
Appeared within the evening peace

When comfort to the poor I bore,
Or when I prayed to God to ease
The anguish of my troubled breast?
Was it not you, O vision blest,
Who rose before me for my sake
In the transparent dark of night?
Not you who came before the break
Of day, invisible, in light,
And spoke to me of hope and love?
Who are you? Guardian from above,
Or wily tempter of my heart?
Oh, speak, and let my doubts depart!
Perhaps it is my vain illusion,
My solitary self-delusion,
And not the fate resolved on high.
Then be it so! From now, the more
My life is lost in yours. I sigh,
I weep, and your defense implore.
Imagine: I am as if alone,
And all my love must die unknown
With none to feel my wearisome
Poor lot, my anguished heart aflame.
I wait: one word from you, one gleam
Of hope will be my solace. Come,
Or break, I pray, this heavy dream
With merited reproof and blame.

    I close. What have I dared to do!
I fear for shame to read it through. . . .
My pledge—your honor and your name,—
And so I trust myself to you. . . .

32

Tatyána heaves a troubled sigh;
She closely grasps the trembling sheet,
And even the rosy wafer[12] dries
Upon her tongue at fever-heat.
From weariness, in paling light,
Her head begins to swim; her thin
Chemise slips lower down her shoulder.
The moon is fading with the night.
Between the moving mists afar
A valley lightens in the morn;
The stream appears a silver gleam;
The breezes bring the shepherd's horn.
The world's astir before the sun,
But to Tatyána all is one.

33

She does not see the dawnlight breaking
Nor seal the letter, but, instead,
Unconscious of the morning hour,
She sits, downcast, with drooping head.
Now opening the door with care,
Her dear old nanny enters softly
To bring a cup of steaming tea.
"It's time, it's time, my darling! There!
You're well awake and up, my Sweet,
Just like an early bird! Last night
I was near death with fear for you.
Praise God, you're looking well and bright.
I'm glad to see your grief is fled;
Your face—a poppy shining red."

34

"I beg you, nanny, do me a favor!"
"Of course, my child! What is it, though?"
"You see ... I fear ... I really do ...
You'll surely blame me. Don't say 'No'."
"God knows I'll serve you willingly."
"Well, have your grandson run at once
And take this note, you know, to him ...
Our neighbor ... do it ... quietly.
He must be careful not to breathe
A word who sent him, do you hear?"
"To whom, my darling? take it where?
I'm getting dull in mind, I fear.
We have so many neighbors call
These days, I scarce can name them all."

35

"Oh, nanny, can't you guess at all?"
"I'm old, my pet. I'm growing old
And feeble, Tanya, in my mind.
I used to do as I was told,
My wits about me ever clear
And lively, Tanya." "Nanny, please,
Your mind is not in question, not
At all. I mean Onegin, dear.
I mean this letter!" "Be it so.
Just don't get cross, but make it plain.
You see, I'm dull and very slow. . . .
What's wrong, my child? Why pale again?"
"Oh, nothing, nothing! Don't delay;
Send off your grandson right away."

36

The day wore on; there was no answer.
Another empty day went by.
From early morning, dressed with care,
Tatyána watched for a reply.
Now Olga's beau came late that day.
"And how's your bosom friend? All well?
It seems he doesn't care to call,"
Tatyána heard her mother say
To him; she trembled, turning red.
"He said he'd come; he's well and hale,"
Thus answered Lensky: "Something has
Detained him, possibly his mail."
Tatyána looked as though she'd heard
A sharp rebuke in every word.

37

At twilight, on the table gleaming,
The samovar stood hissing hot,
While gently, in a cloud of vapor,
The tea was brewed in a china pot.
Then Olga busily set out,
Behind a row of shining cups,
To pour the fragrant tea, the while
A house-boy served the cream about.
Beside the window, breathing on
The pane, Tatyána could but linger,
Lost in her anxious reverie.
She waited; with her little finger
She traced on misted glass a row
Of hallowed letters, *E* and *O*.

38

Yet all the while her heart was aching,
Her weary eyes half blind with tears.
The sound of hoofs! . . . Her heart stood still.
He's nearer . . . at the front! . . . She hears
Onegin! . . . Oh, like a spectre light
Tatyána springs into the hall,
From porch to yard, to vanish soon
Deep in the garden in her flight.
On, on she flies, nor dares to glance
Behind; across a lane she flashes,
Then past the bridge, and brake; then on
Through alleys to the lake she dashes,
Through shrubs and lilac-bushes fast,
Where, panting, on a bench at last

39

She falls! . . .
         "He's here! Onegin,—here!
O God! What did he think of me?"
But still her anguished spirit guards
A dim blind hope of what might be.
She trembles, ready to suppose
He'd look for her: Does no one come?
She hears the serving-maids at song
While picking berries in the close.
By cunning masters they were bidden
To sing at work (lest they should try,
However berries might abound,
To eat a few upon the sly,—
A rural shrewd device to stop
Them plundering the berry-crop).

THE MAIDENS' SONG

Come, sweet lassies, come away!
Come, my darlings, come to play!
Let us play together all,
Let us dance till evenfall,
Let us sing a pretty song,
Sing a magic choral song.
Lure a lad into the ring
Where the roundelay we sing.
When we lure the lad away
To our dance and roundelay,
When we lure the curly lad,
Hurl red cherries at his head,
Fend him off with raspberries,
Berries of the currant-trees.
Never come around to spy
When our magic words we say;
Never come around to spy
When we dance the roundelay.

with eyes aglow
Onegin at the turning stood

40

Tatyána listens to their voices,
All but unheeding to their shrill
Resounding song, yet cannot make
Her wildly throbbing heart be still,
Or wait for flaming cheeks to smart
No longer; from her deep emotion
Still brighter flame her glowing cheeks
And louder beats her pounding heart.
Thus a poor butterfly will flutter,
Snared by a schoolboy's net, and beat
Its iridescent wings in vain;
Thus quakes a hare in winter wheat
In sudden terror when it spies
The covert where the hunter lies.

41

At last Tatyána, gently sighing,
Rose from the lonely bench to go.
There, as she started slowly down
The garden path, with eyes aglow
Onegin at the turning stood.
She faltered, terrified, as though
Seared by a shaft of flame, by some
Dread apparition from the wood.
But this encounter and its sequel
I shall relate at greater length
When I am equal to the task,
When I regain my skill and strength.
Another day I'll try my best,
But now I feel I need some rest.

Chapter Four

La morale est dans la nature des choses.
                                        Necker

(1-6) 7

The less we care in a love affair
The more we move a woman's heart
And are the surer to undo her
With every new seductive art.
Time was when, bold beyond all measure,
We made of lechery a science,
And trumpeted abroad the feats
And triumphs of a loveless pleasure.
But such enjoyments seem more suited
To old baboons and fools at last:[1]
The days of Lovelace's renown
Have long since vanished in the past
Along with styles no more in use—
Majestic wigs and red-heeled shoes.

8

Who would not sicken of imposture
And harping on a single phrase,
Of proving things that have been proved
So many times in solemn ways;
Of hearing outcries of despair,
Of vanquishing a prejudice
That even thirteen-year-old girls
Would hardly tolerate or care
To keep? And who would not be bored
By threats, affected fears, and lies,
By letters running to six pages,
By gossip, tears, by watchful eyes
Of aunts and mothers prying still,
And husband's wearisome good-will?

9

Such were Onegin's firm opinions,
For he has from his youth, of old,
Been oft the victim of delusion
And passions wild and uncontrolled.
A pampered youth, a little while
He was by pleasure captivated,
Till, disenchanted by desire,
By cheap success and worldly guile,
He heard the murmur of a still
Sad voice in his solitude; faint
With boredom, deep within himself
He knew the soul's immortal plaint—
That he had lost eight years of time,
The fairest flower of his prime.

10

He was no longer lured by love;
At times he courted, glad enough
To free himself at each betrayal
And live consoled at each rebuff.
He sought fair ladies without zest,
Deserted them without regret,
Glad to forget their love or hate.
Just so a casual, heedless guest,
Appearing late for evening whist,
Decides it is enough to play
A hand or two, or none at all,
And calmly leave upon his way
To bed; he does not care to know
Where next at evening he may go.

11

But Tanya's letter stirred Onegin
With an unwonted sympathy;
The language of her maiden fancy
Aroused a swarm of reverie.
He called to mind Tatyána's sad
Pale face, her melancholy air;
A dream of purest rapture filled
His heart, and made his spirit glad.
Perhaps her letter roused old passions
Held long at bay, or old-time lust,
But he resolved he would requite
Her simple innocence and trust.
Now let us hasten to the place
Where he met Tatyána face to face.

12

A moment passed without a word.
Then, drawing near, Onegin said:
"I had your letter; do not try
To disavow it now. I read
Your heart's pure trust in every word
You wrote. Your love, your confidence
In me, sincere and unaffected,
Have long unspoken feelings stirred.
I do not come to praise your action,
But would your trust in me repay
In words as artless and sincere
By my own confession now. I pray
That you accept my earnest plea,
Then think just what you may of me.

13

"Had but a narrow life of pure
Domestic pleasure been my goal;
Or had the kindly fates decreed
A husband's and a father's role;
Had I but simply to decide
On bringing up a family,—
Believe, I should have asked for none
But one like you to be my bride.
I speak without conceits to you:
I should have chosen you alone
To share my mournful life with me
As my first dream of youth, my own
Dear pledge of all things true and good,
And been as happy . . . as I could!

14

"But I'm by nature and by fate
Not made for joy, I must confess.
I don't deserve the qualities
You bring, your gifts of happiness.
Believe, I speak in conscience true.
For both of us the married state
Would end in boredom and in anguish,
However great my love for you.
My heart would cool, and should you weep,
You'd never move my heart to ruth
But only make me chafe with anger.
What sort of love, to tell the truth,
Our life for many years would be,
And to what end—for you and me?

15

"What home on earth can sadder be
Than one in which a cheerless wife
Must grieve by day and night, alone,
For one unworthy of her life;
In which a husband wearily,
Though knowing well her many virtues,
Reviles his fate, and, sullen, comes
In anger, frowning gloomily?
And I am such. What were your dreams
When, in your innocence, you wrote
With such great purity of heart
And mind to me that artless note?
Shall such a life of grief and hate
Become your inevitable fate?

16

"I'll never now regain my soul,
My best of life . . . it cannot be!
I love you with a brother's love,
Perhaps more true, more tenderly.
Then be not angered when I say
A girl may more than once surrender
Her heart unto a passing dream,
Yet wake to love another day,
Just as a tree renews its leaves
Each season. Such is heaven's will.
I understand your deeper feelings,
But others could betray you. . . . Still,
You know the world must understand,
Then school yourself in self-command."

17

In earnest thus Onegin preached.[2]
Scarce breathing, Tanya, tearfully,
Half-blinded, unprotesting, heard
His kindly-spoken homily.
He offered her his hand. Despairing,
(Mechanically, as they say)
She took his arm in silence, grave
And melancholy in her bearing.
They walked on homeward through the garden;
And, as they entered arm in arm
Together, no one turned to look
At them or thought of any harm.
Our rural freedom has its rights,
As real as Moscow's proud delights.

18

Onegin acted well, dear reader,
In this affair, you must agree,
And proved himself to sad Tatyána
The soul of true nobility
And feeling, though some people may
Condemn him harshly in their spite,
Suspicion, and relentless blame.
Both friends and enemies, I say,
(And possibly they mean the same)
Maligned his name. It well may be
We must have enemies to face
But from my friends—deliver me,
Good Lord! I know their worthy ends,
Yet save me from my so-called friends.

19

My meaning? Well, just so. Perhaps
I'd lull my gloomy thoughts to sleep
And hint, as in parentheses,
There is no calumny so deep,
There is no sort of stupid sham,
No fancy of the basest born
And sanctioned by the better classes;
No slander, vulgar epigram,
That some good friend will not repeat
In decent circles, with a smile,
With something added on his own
With undesigning spite or guile—
Because he loves you in his heart,
And, like your kin, he takes your part.

There is no calumny so deep,
There is no sort of stupid sham . . .
That some good friend will not repea
In decent circles, with a smile

104

20

Ahem! And now, my gentle reader,
Are all your relatives quite well?
Perhaps it will not be amiss
To have your faithful servant tell
Just what by that he has in mind:
Our relatives are folk whom we
Are bound by duty to revere,
Defer to, honor, love in kind,
And then, as custom bids us do,
To visit on each Christmas Day
Or else congratulate by mail,
So that on other days they may
Forget us for at least one year. . . .
God grant them days of health and cheer!

21

But if your friends are changeable,
You may depend upon the fair
And count upon the rights of love
Through stormy weather and despair!
No doubt. But what of vain renown,
The whims of fashion, wayward feelings,
The snares of high society?
The sex, they say, is light as down.
What's more, a husband's least opinions
Are heeded by a faithful wife
By words and acts at any cost;
And yet your dearest love in life
Is in a flash enticed away,
For love is oft the devil's play.

22

Then where should one his trust and love
Bestow? And who will not deceive?
And who in words and acts will follow
The standards which we all believe?
Who sows no slander to exalt
Himself? Who does not lie about us?
Who holds a friend in constant love?
Who will forgive a trifling fault?
No, no! Why chase a phantom shape?
Dear reader, spare yourself more pain
And cherish your own self! Have done
With striving for a dream in vain!
Then make your life, your own dear name
Your worthy cause and rightful aim.

23

The sequel of Tatyána's tryst?
Alas, the end's not hard to guess!
The pangs of love still fiercely stirred
Her soul athirst for happiness;
Her soul, in hopeless desolation,
In all the emptiness about her,
Endured a burning grief,—her heart
Bereft of peace and consolation.
Her bloom of life and loveliness,
Her smile, her virgin calm, had passed.
They vanished like an empty sound.
Poor Tanya's youth was fading fast:
Thus heavy storms enshroud the morn
When day is struggling to be born.

24

Alas, Tatyána droops in silence;
She droops as fades a flame at night
Within the gloom; dispirited,
She looks at nothing with delight.
And knowingly the neighbors wag
Their heads in whispered conversations:
"High time to marry her, high time!"
But I must stop. I should not drag
My story out. I'll please your fancy
With scenes of love and happiness.
And yet I cannot in my pity
Leave Tanya out in her distress.
Forgive me: I have always been
In love with this dear heroine.

25

From day to day yet more enamoured
By Olga's grace—so fair was she,—
Poor Lensky yielded up his heart
To her in sweet captivity.
Together they at eventide
Would sit secluded in her room,
Or, in the garden through the morning,
They'd wander slowly side by side.
But think of it! Sometimes by love
Enchanted, once in a great while,
He'd venture shyly, tenderly,
Emboldened by dear Olga's smile,
To dally with a curling tress
Or kiss the border of her dress.

26

Sometimes he'd read aloud to Olga
A novel in a moral vein,
Fit for her sex far better than
Chateaubriand in his domain.
And, blushing, he would skip a page
Or two of some immodest matter
He thought unsuited to a mind
As pure as Olga's at her age.
Or, from the family secluded,
Lost in a game of chess, the pair
Would sit absorbed, preoccupied,
Deep pondering a move with care,
Till Lensky, blandly smiling, took
With his own pawn, alas! his rook.

27

And too, at home, his Olga's image
Absorbed his hours of leisure there
And made him fill her album pages
With sketches done with utmost care.
He drew some doves upon a lute,
Some country scenes, a rustic tomb,
A shrine to sacred Aphrodite,
In pen or color that would suit.
Below some signature inscribed
By other hands, he'd write a line
Of tender verse for Olga's eyes,
As witness of his dream divine
And fleeting thoughts that would endure
Through time and change forever pure.

28

Of course you've seen the albums kept
By girls in each provincial town
And found them scrawled by girlhood friends
From start to finish, up and down.
Their hackneyed and erratic rhymes,
Made sadder by mistakes in spelling
And phrases of eternal friendship,
Have been abused since olden times.
Qu'écrirez-vous sur ces tablettes?
Upon the first page you will find,
And *toute à vous, Annette* behind it,
And on the last page, underlined,
*Who loves you more than I should write
Another line for your delight.*

29

There, too, infallibly you'll find
Two hearts, a torch, a wreath, a bloom,
And many vows of touching love
Till death us part beyond the tomb.
There army captains at the end
Have gibed with caustic army wit;
And there I, too, have often scrawled
A pleasant word or two, my friend,
For I was certain that my lines
And foolishness would win meanwhile
Delighted glances in return:
For who would, in the future, smile
Or bother gravely to decide
How cleverly, or why, I lied?

30

But you, odd albums of the devil's
Own library, in fine array;
You albums, richly bound, that vex
The common rhymsters of today,
Though you reveal at every turn
The signs of Tolstoy's clever brush,[3]
The grace of Baratynsky's verse,[4]
May lightning blast your pages, burn
You all to ash at any time!
When some illustrious *grande dame*
Brings out her quarto for my pen,
I long to write an epigram
In hate, in anger, yet I shall
Be asked to write a madrigal.

I long to write an epigram
In hate, in anger, yet I shall
Be asked to write a madrigal

III

31

But Lensky wrote no madrigals
For lovely Olga's benefit,
His verse devoted to his passion
Unstained by lines of sparkling wit.
Dear Olga's looks, his constant theme;
Dear Olga's words, his living truth,—
A tide of elegiac verse
In their simplicity supreme.
Thus, too, your heart of passion burns,
Inspired Yazýkov,[5] when your Muse
In precious elegies rehearses
In praise of beauty, God knows whose;
Perhaps the essence of your fate
Will be revealed at some far date.

32

But hush! You hear? Our sternest critic[6]
Now bids us fling away for good
Our humble elegiac laurels.
And thus he chides our brotherhood
Of rhyming bards: "When will you drop
Your weary weeping, drop your quacking,
Your whimpering of 'days of yore'?
Enough! Chant other tunes, or stop!"
"You're right! But surely you'd reveal
The classic trumpet, sword, and mask,[7]
And bid us bring to life the funds
Of dead old knowledge as our task,—
Correct?" But no, he frets again:
"Write odes, odes only, gentlemen,

33

As they were written in the days
Made famous in the long ago."
"Look here, you mean majestic odes
And only those? You well should know
What our keen satirist[8] once said
About your musty rhetoric
Far duller than our elegists
Could do about the living dead."
"Your lyric songs are trifling things,
Too pitiful in sense, inane,
But odes are lofty, nobly formed!"
I stand aside. I must restrain
Myself, nor set at odds our great
Two ages in a hot debate.

34

But Lensky, pledged to liberty
And fame, would have been glad to plead
His stormy cause by writing odes,
Had Olga only cared to read
His verse at all. Lives there a bold
True poet but hankers to rehearse
His tearful verse before the charmer
His soul adores? The world can hold
No richer gift. Blessed the lover
Who reads his visionary theme
Before a silent languid beauty,
The object of his song and dream!
And yet, when all is said and done,
She prefers another kind of fun.

35

For me, I read my harmonies
Of lyric poetry and lays
Before my dear old nurse alone,
The darling of my childhood days.
Or when by chance a guest appears
To share with me my lonely dinner,
I grab him by his coat lapels
And spout my drama in his ears;[9]
Or else when sad at heart or worn
By rhymes (I do not mean to jest),
I wander by my lake and flush
The wild ducks from their reedy nest:
On hearing my sweet-resounding lay,
They rise, alarmed, and fly away.

(36) 37

But what's Onegin doing? Friends,
I crave your patience. By the way,
I will, to please you, now describe
The occupations of his day.
He lived a hermit's life. He took
To getting up at seven throughout
The summer months; then, lightly clad,
He sauntered to the hillside brook,
And there, like Gülnare's bard, he swam
That Hellespont of his from shore
To shore.[10] Back home, he sipped his coffee
While skimming journals read before,
And next he dressed[11].....................
....

(38) 39

Long ramblings, books, and sound good sleep;
The bubbling brook, the woodland shade;
At times a fresh young kiss in secret
At meeting with a dark-eyed maid;
A restive horse restrained at will;
A dinner delicately planned;
A bottle of some good light wine;
The solitude of evenings still
With peace serene,—became, in fine,
Onegin's solitary lot
While summer days went brightly by
In languid ease, and he forgot
His city friends, their bustling noise,
The boredom of their empty joys.

40

But our northern summer season,
Like southern winter, flashes by
Before we hardly know it's gone,—
A fact we earnestly deny.
The tang of autumn's in the air;
The sunny hours grow ever rarer
Each passing day; the sky is clouded;
The woods are solitary, bare,
And sad with mournful murmurings.
The mists above the fields lie white;
The shrilling caravans of geese
Stretch far to southward; in the night,
Now gloomier and desolate,
November's knocking at the gate.

41

The mornings rise in haze and cold;
The fields that hummed with work of late
Lie still; the hungry wolf comes out
To hunt beside his hungry mate,
And, scenting him, the plodding bay
Snorts, and the wary traveler
Soon dashes on uphill. No more
The herding boy at break of day
Will drive the cows from out their sheds;
No more his horn at noon will bring
Them in a ring. The peasant maidens[12]
Spin their flax, while they chat or sing
Beside the crackling matchwood light
That cheers them in the wintry night.

42

And now the frosts begin to snap
In silver fields of early snows
(To please the reader with a rhyme
I tally early *snows* with *rose*).
Now brighter in its winter joys,
The river's like a parquet floor
Where crowds of happy boys on skates
Engrave the ice with ringing noise;
There, hoping still to swim the stream,
A waddling goose on small red feet
Steps forth with caution on the ice
But slips and topples in retreat.
Now snowflakes spin rank after rank
And fall in stars upon the bank.

43

How can one pass the time in pleasure
In country wilds? Go rambling there?
It makes one weary staring at
The naked sameness everywhere.
To gallop over fields of ice?
Your horse on blunted shoes might trip
On treacherous uneven ground
And founder headlong in a trice.
To stay in loneliness indoors
And read de Pradt[13] or Walter Scott?
No books? Then check accounts or lose
Your temper, drink, and, like as not,
The night will pass, tomorrows too,
And so the whole of winter through.

44

Onegin, like a true Childe Harold,
Prefers to laze about and brood.
He takes his icy bath on waking
And stays at home in solitude
All day, in idle meditation,
Or, with a cue and just two balls,
For hours around the billiard-table
He finds a restful occupation.
But, by the time the fields are veiled
In dusk, he puts his cue away.
He waits before the open fire
For Lensky, driven in his sleigh
With three roan horses, to appear:
Then welcome dinner, welcome cheer!

45

And now Moët or Veuve Cliquot,
A wine regarded as the best,
Chilled in their bottles on the ice,
Appears in honor of the guest.
Like Hippocrene it gleams in light,
And all its froth and sparkling play
Arouse in me (symbolical
Of this or that) a great delight.
I gave my last of meager coins
For bottled wine, all I was worth!
Do you remember, friends, do you,
What endless follies and what mirth
Came with its bubbling magic stream?
What talk and verse? O happy dream!

And now Moët or Veuve Cliquot,
Chilled in their bottles on the ice,
Appears in honor of the guest.

46

But now its effervescence plays
My poor digestion false, and so
I'm minded to prefer today
The sensible and safe Bordeaux.
Champagne is out: Aÿ[14] is bright,
Seductive, gay in company,
But still a mistress at its best,
Too risky, frivolous, and light.
But you, Bordeaux, at any time
Are like a friend we always treasure,
A friend prepared to comfort us
In grief, misfortune, hours of leisure,
On lonely or on happy days.
I sing, O friend Bordeaux, your praise!

47

The fire is out. Grey ashes veil
The gold of glowing coals; a few
Fine threads of vapor drift in air;
The hearth is breathing warmth into
The darkening room. Two pipes of fine
Tobacco send their rings of smoke
Into the chimney-place. Two goblets
Still brightly gleam with bubbling wine
Upon the board. . . . The shadows come,
And night. . . . (I like the friendly glass,
The friendly evening hour of talk
We Russians in the twilight pass,
The hour we call twixt wolf-and-dog.)[15]
Let's hear the party's dialogue.

48

"How are your neighbors? How's Tatyána?
And lively Olga, how is she?"
"Pour me another glass—just half—
There, that's enough. . . . The family
Are really well, quite well. They send
Regards. Oh, Olga's neck and bosom,
I say, are lovelier each day!
And what a spirit! . . . As a friend,
I urge you make another visit;
You called there twice, but not for long.
Look in another time. You know
Yourself such negligence is wrong.
The dunce I am! . . . They bade me say
Be sure to come next Saturday."

49

"I?" "Yes, of course! Tatyána's party.
In fact, her nameday celebration.
Her mother wants you, Olga too;
You can't refuse their invitation."
"They'll have a mob, I'm bound to say,
The sort of company I hate!"
"No, hardly anyone, I'm sure!
Only the nearest kin. I pray
You'll come. Oblige me, as a favor!
Say, yes!" "All right." "You're very fine!"
And, pleased, in honor of his Olga
He drained another glass of wine,
And spread himself, as lovers do,
About dear Olga's charms anew.

50

His heart was gay. The day was set.
When but two weeks of time had fled,
The sweets of marriage would be his,
The secrets of the nuptial bed,
The crowning joys that wedlock brings.
He never in his rapture dreamed
What cares and sorrows he would face,
What weariness of daily things.
While we, as Hymen's foes, present
The married state as one long scene
Of boredom, like a dull romance
Of Lafontaine,[16] a sad routine,
Poor Lensky, innocent at heart,
Was made for a domestic part.

51

He was beloved . . . or so at least
He fancied,—happy in his bliss.
Blessed the man who's blindly faithful,
Who will all reasoning dismiss
And hug the rapture of the hour;
He's like a wine-dazed wayfarer
Come safe to bed at last, or like
A butterfly sunk in a flower.
But wretched he whose mind no fond
Illusion holds, who comes to hate
Each free, untutored word or motion,
Who would each mood anticipate,
Whose heart is daily turned to stone
By doubt and fear of the unknown.

He was beloved . . . or so at least
He fancied,— happy in his bliss.

Chapter Five

Do not dream those fearful dreams,
O thou, my sweet Svetlána!

Zhukóvsky

I

That year the autumn season lingered
Till almost Christmastime while all
Were waiting, waiting with impatience
For winter snow; it did not fall
Till January third, at night.
Tatyána, up at early dawn,
Could see the roofs and fences, yards
And gardens blanketed in white;
The window-panes with flowers of frost,
The trees in silvery array,
The pinewood softly glistening
In hoar, and yards with magpies gay.
All white lay carpeted each hill;
In shining light the world lay still.

2

Winter! . . . The peasant-man, rejoicing,
Breaks fresh the highway with his sleigh;
His pony, sniffing the new snow,
Trots easily along the way.
A post-chaise passes in a flash
And flings up high the furrowed snow;
The coachman sits upon his box
In sheepskin coat and scarlet sash.
A serf-boy, fancying himself
A prancing horse, comes racing bold
Across the yard, a small black dog
Upon his sled. All stiff with cold,
The scamp can at the window see
His mother, scolding warningly.

3

Perhaps you would dismiss such scenes
As things too trifling to attract
The cultured mind, as commonplace,
As but a low prosaic fact.
Another poet, by gods divine
Inspired, knew how to glorify
The first pure snow and winter joy
With dazzling hues in every line
He wrote.[1] I'm sure he could delight
Your heart with glowing poetry
About some secret rides in sleighs;
I shall not strive in rivalry
With him, nor yet with one who paid
His homage to the Finnish maid.[2]

4

Tatyána, Russian in her feelings,
Not knowing quite her reason why,
Delighted in the Russian winter
And splendor of the earth and sky:
The sparkling frost, the revelry,
The sleighing on a wintry day,
The snows in rosy sunset gleaming,
And nights before Epiphany,
Which in their customary way
The Larins used to celebrate.[3]
The serving-maids then came to read
Through charms the ladies' coming fate
And wish each year for each the same—
A spouse of military fame.

5

Tatyána trusted in her heart
The folkways of an age gone by;
She knew what dreams and cards foretold,
And what the moon might signify.
She quaked at omens with new fear,
Saw everywhere some mystery
With hidden warnings of misfortune
And signs of danger coming near:
That tomcat, when he licked his paws
And washed his face beside the stove,
Was an unfailing sign to her
That guests were coming; if above
Her suddenly, at her left side,
The new moon's crescent she espied,

6

Tatyána trembled and grew pale.
Or, if a shooting star flashed by
Across the night and disappeared
In golden dust, she'd quickly try,
While still she watched the rolling fire,
To whisper in her great excitement
Her heart's most sacred cherished wish.
But if she met a black-robed friar,
Or if a hare had streaked across
The road from field to field in flight,
Beside herself with sudden fear
She'd stop, not knowing what it might
Forebode, and in her dread she'd wait
For blows of certain evil fate.

7

Thus every terror held for her
Its own revealing secret charm:
We're all by nature prone to feel
With greater zest each new alarm.
Then Yuletide's here! O what delight!
The young by omens read their fortunes,
For flighty youth appears carefree
When future years lie gleaming bright
In boundless time. The aged then
Through spectacles begin to peer
Ahead, although their lives are past
Retrieving and the grave is near.
No matter: lisping hopes can still
Awake with lies a childish thrill.

8

Tatyána watches, fascinated,
To see the melted wax assume
Strange patterns in the bowl of water,
Predicting happiness or doom.
How all enraptured servants long
To bring up from the bowl their rings!
And when Tatyána takes her own,
She hears them sing the ancient song:
There peasant folk are rich as kings
And scoop up silver with a spade;
All glory to the lucky lad,
And glory to the lucky maid.
The song rings sad of something lost;
The girls prefer the *cat-song* most.[4]

9

A frosty night. The sky shines bright;
The wondrous hosts of starry spheres
Sail gently in their cloudy seas.
Tatyána in the yard appears
In a low-cut frock, and turns her own
Small mirror toward the waning moon;
But trembling in the mirror's face,
There gleams the wistful moon alone. . . .
The crunch of snow. . . . Someone's coming!
She tiptoes toward him as on wings;
More tender than a reed, her voice
Upon the midnight softly rings:
"What is your name?" He hurries on,
But first he mumbles, "Agafón."[5]

Tatyána, as her nurse had counseled,
Prepared to read her fate that night.
She ordered ready in the bath-house
A table laid for two; but fright
Assailed her suddenly. I, too,
Remembering our poor Svetlána,[6]
Grew fearful of this sorcery:
I would not have Tatyána rue
Her fate through me. At last she went
To bed, her silken sash unlaced,
And Lel[7] soon hovered overhead.
But neath her downy pillow placed,
Her maiden mirror lay. Now deep
The night. Tatyána's fast asleep.

11

Tatyána dreams a wondrous dream.
She dreams she's walking in a glade
Across a snowy meadowland
Shrouded in gloomy mist and shade.
She hears a river boil and roar
And whirl its waters, seething dark
And grey, ice-free in deepest winter,
Among the snowdrifts piled before
Her high. Two slender poles joined by
The ice are flung across the stream
And made a bridge of death that spanned
The raging torrent. In her dream,
She stood bewildered and in doubt,
Shut in by darkness all about.

12

Tatyána fretted at the river
That blocked her way; her heart then sank
For not a friendly hand appeared
To help her reach the further bank.
Just then a drift begins to stir,
And lo! from underneath the snow
Comes forth a huge, a shaggy bear.
She screams; he bellows back at her;
He offers her his great sharp paw.
She frees herself from her alarm
And, trembling, gathering her strength,
She leans upon the monster's arm—
To cross the rushing stream. Alack!
The bear still follows in her track.

13

Not daring once to glance around,
She runs before the dreadful shape,
But from her hateful shaggy servant
In vain she struggles to escape.
He lunges forward, growling, close
Behind. All stern and motionless
A grove of firs and birches rises
In sombre beauty, deep in snows,
Their tufted branches bending low.
The stars alone are shining bright
Aloft between high birch and lime
And aspen bare within the night.
The road is lost; ravine and steep
In drifts of snow lie buried deep.

14

She gains the wood, the bear behind her;
She sinks up to her knees in snow.
A branch droops low and twines itself
Around her neck, plucks at one blow
Her golden earrings. Now her small
Wet shoe she loses, stuck in banks
Of snow; then, too, her handkerchief
She drops and has no time at all
To pick it up. Hearing the bear
Still lunging on, she dares not lift
Her trailing skirt, for shame and fear,
To help her get across the drift.
She runs; he follows hard upon
Her trail until her strength is gone.

15

She falls, exhausted; then alertly
The shaggy monster seizes her;
Submissive, almost in a faint,
She scarce can draw a breath, or stir.
He drags her past a forest close
When, at a turning, suddenly
Within the snow-bound wilderness
Between the trees a hovel shows.
One window glimmers in the night.
Loud yells and din resound within
The hut. The bear grunts out: "Come here
And warm yourself; they are my kin."
And in the hallway, through a door,
He lays her on the threshold floor.

16

When she comes to, Tatyána looks
Around, but does not see the beast;
She hears wild shouts and glasses clinking
As at some famous funeral feast.
They squeal and hoot. There's no escape.
She peers with caution through a chink
And sees, amazed, around a table
A throng of strange and monstrous shape:
One is a savage dog with horns;
One has a rooster's head, and one
Seems like a witch, a bearded goat;
A pig sits next a skeleton;
Then bobtailed dwarfs and creatures that
Appear to be half crane, half cat.

17

And here she spies, most dreadful yet,
A crawfish on a spider's back!
And there, a skull in a scarlet cap
Revolving on a goose-like neck!
And there alone, a windmill dancing
A jig with flapping, rattling wings!
Song, laughter, barking, whistling, sounds
Of human speech and horses' prancing!
But what could Tanya think when she
Beheld among the monsters here
The very hero of our novel,—
The man she loved and held in fear!
He sat at table midst the roar
About, and slyly watched the door.

18

A sign from him, they screech together;
He drinks, as one they howl and swill;
He laughs, they all explode in laughter;
He frowns, and all of them are still.
He seems among this company
Their master. Then, more confident,
Tatyána pushes slow against
The door, so curious is she. . . .
A sudden gust of wind blows out
The lanterns in a flash; complete
Confusion falls upon the throng.
Onegin rises from his seat
With eyes afire. The demons roar.
Onegin stalks across the floor.

19

And now with terror in her heart,
Tatyána struggles to take flight,
But cannot stir; in vain she tries
To rise, to flee, to scream in fright.
Onegin then flings wide the door;
The multitude of raging fiends
Behold with shrieks of frenzied laughter
The maiden faint with fear before
Their gaze. Their eyes ablaze, their hoofs
And horns, their crooked snouts and paws,
Their blood-red tongues, sharp teeth and nails,
Their tufted tails, their bony claws,—
All point at her with dreadful whine
And savage hoot: "She's mine! She's mine!"

"She's mine!" Onegin cries in wrath.

20

"She's mine!" Onegin cries in wrath.
Then suddenly the throngs had flown,
And in the frosty dark of night
He stands beside the maid alone.
He gently draws his coveted
Tatyána toward a shaky bench,
Bids her lie down, and quietly
Upon her shoulder leans his head.
Then Olga enters of a sudden,
And Lensky next. A flash of light!
Onegin wildly dares his two
Unbidden guests, prepared to smite
With seething hatred in his breath;
But Tanya lies as pale as death.

21

Their quarrel swells. Onegin draws
His dagger, strikes, and Lensky falls.
A cry of torment! Darker yet,
Dread shadows creep along the walls.
The cottage shakes. From dreams of pain
Tatyána in her terror wakes. . . .
She looks; her room is bright with day,
And through the frosty window-pane
The crimson rays of morning glow.
Then, rosier than morning light,
Dear Olga bursts into the room,
Swift as a swallow in her flight.
"What did you dream?" all breathlessly
She asks: "Whom, Tanya, did you see?"

22

But she, of Olga scarce aware,
Lay silent, book in hand, in bed;
Page after page she slowly turned
But not a single word she said.
Her book contained no painted scene,
No revelation of great wisdom,
No poet's vain and sweet invention.
Not either Virgil or Racine,
Or Seneca or Scott or Byron,
Or modern fashion-plates, in brief,
Could hold Tatyána half as much
As did Martýn Zadéka, chief
Of the Chaldean seers, it seems,
The great interpreter of dreams.[8]

23

It happened that a peddler brought
Into their village one fine day
This ancient monumental volume,
Which Tanya purchased, with a stray
Old copy of *Malvine*[9] (her set
Was incomplete), for three and fifty.
He took, to equalize the bargain,
Two Petriads,[10] an alphabet,
A grammar, a book of hackneyed fables,
And volume three of Marmontel.[11]
Zadéka soon became her treasure,
Her constant favorite, as well
Her solace and her comforter
That always went to bed with her.

24

Tatyána could not understand
Her dream nor settle in her mind
What fate the dreadful night forebode,
Which she was now resolved to find.
She searched the index carefully
For words in alphabetic order—
Bear, Blizzard, Bridge, Cottage, Dagger,
Then Darkness, Door, Fir, Raven, Tree,—
But searched in vain. Her fears and doubts
The wise Zadéka could not still,
And yet instinctively she knew
Her dream foreshadowed only ill.
For some few days her mournful mood
Grew darker in disquietude.

25

But lo! from out the morning valley
The 'rosy fingers' of the sun[12]
Blaze forth Tatyána's nameday feast.
From dawn the house is overrun
With guests from every neighborhood
For miles around, arriving in
Their coaches, sledges, carry-alls,
With servants, nurses, and their brood.
They mill and jostle in the halls;
They crowd inside the drawing-room
With cries of greeting, laughter, hugs,
With bark of dogs, the constant boom
And hum of voices, scraping feet,
While nurses scold and children weep.

26

Here with his portly wife arrives
Big-bellied Pustyakóv; then sure
Gvozdín, a tough old farmer, owner
Of peasants miserably poor;
Then two Skotínins, white as snow,
With all their progeny from two
To thirty summers at the top;
Then Petushkóv, the district beau;
Then in his vizored cap, unshaven,
My own first cousin, dear Buyánov[13]
(I think you know the chap), and next
That former counselor, old Flyánov,
A hardened gossip, cheat, and loon,
A glutton, grafter, and buffoon.

27

Monsieur Triquet was in the party
That came along with Kharlikóv,—
A sly old wit, in his ginger wig
And spectacles, late from Tambóv.
And, like a true-blue Frenchman, he
Had brought a song to grace the day,
Set to the childhood melody:
Réveillez-vous, belle endormie![14]
Triquet had found his lucky ditty
Lost in a yellowed almanac;
Then, like a bold sagacious bard,
He had resolved to bring it back
To life—by cutting *belle Nina*
And singing forth *belle Tatiana.*

28

Now from the army post nearby
The captain of the company
Drives up, each mother's fondest hope,
Each spinster's bright divinity.
The news he brings! What great delight!
The regimental band will play:
The colonel's sending it himself!
There'll be a ball, this very night!
The wenches skip about for joy.
But dinner first. The couples proud
Move to the table, arm in arm;
The girls beside Tatyána crowd.
They cross themselves for meat and wine,
And, buzzing, then sit down to dine.

29

All chatter ends. They're busily
Engaged. They chew. On every side
The pleasant clank of plates and forks
And chime of glasses. Satisfied,
By slow degrees they hum and boom
With laughter, squeals, and argument;
Yet none can hear his neighbor out,
So loud the clatter in the room.
Then suddenly a door flies open,
And Lensky enters with his friend
Onegin. The hostess cries: "At last!
Oh, dear!" The guests move over, lend
A plate or knife or glass, and seat
The two arrivals at their meat.

30

They place them opposite Tatyána.
Grown paler than the moon at dawn,
She cannot raise her timid eyes
But trembles like a hunted fawn.
With fever, pale from stifled fears,
She burns, feels cold, then sick at heart;
She does not hear their words of greeting;
She struggles to keep back her tears
Before the guests. She dreads, poor thing,
She may at any moment faint.
But she regains her self-possession
And answers softly with restraint
In greeting Lensky and his friend.
She stays at table to the end.

31

All show of nerves and tragic airs,
Young women's fainting-spells and tears,
Onegin had for long detested
And had resented them for years.
That queer good chap was angered at
The company of guests he hated,
And, noting Tanya's agitation,
He swore he'd trim poor Lensky flat
For luring him away from home.
He frowned in sullen indignation,
Vowing to drive the poet mad;
And pleased by this anticipation,
He set his mind to think up jests
Caricaturing all the guests.

32

True, other guests had also noted
Tatyána's plight, but every eye
And all the talk around the table
Were centered on a fat, rich pie
(Alas, too salty), all glad to greet
As a fit conclusion to the roast
The tar-sealed bottles of champagne,
And drink a toast, before the sweet.
There came a row of slim tall glasses,
As slender as your waist, Zizi,[15]
O fairest crystal of my soul,
My lure, my theme for poetry.
For many lovesick happy days,
Drunk with my love, I sang your praise.

33

The bottle pops; the red wine sputters,
Released at last. The sparkling wine
Stirs every heart. Triquet arises,
Long tortured by his song divine.
He gravely waits. The company
Lean forward in respectful silence.
Tatyána scarcely breathes. Triquet
Turns, facing her, and sings off-key
The couplets one by one. Applause
And shouts around the singer burst.
Tatyána's forced to curtsy to
The lofty poet. He toasts her first
Of all, and with a gesture grand
He puts his verses in her hand.

34

Tatyána thanked them for their toasts,
Their praise, and answered each one fair.
But when his turn arrived, Onegin,
Who marked the girl's embarrassed air,
Her great fatigue, her languidness,
Was moved to pity in his heart:
Without a spoken word he bowed
To her, and yet with tenderness
His glance was wonderfully kind.
Perhaps his heart was moved to still
Her fears, or flirt perhaps from habit,
Or prove to her his own good will.
His tender look of sympathy
Stirred Tanya's heart with ecstasy.

35

The chairs were noisily pushed back;
They crowd into the drawing room
Like bees that leave their luscious hive
For meadows sweet with summer bloom.
Contented with their feast, some look
For corners where to drowse or chat;
The matrons seek the fireplace;
The girls, a more secluded nook
To whisper in. The green-baize tables
Attract the gamesters to engage
Their eager skills in Whist, but l'Ombre
And Boston are preferred by age:
Such games are boredom's progeny,
One greed-begotten family.

36

Eight rubbers have the champions
Of Whist played off; eight times by rote
They've changed their places in the game.
Then tea is served. We like to note
In country wilds the time of day
By tea and dinner, guided by
Our appetites unerringly;
The stomach is our best Brequet.
But let me add, in passing merely,
That in my poetry I mention
Great feasts of wine and sundry foods,
And treat them with as much attention
As godlike Homer does, the lord
Whom thirty centuries adored.

(37-38) 39

But here is tea. The girls have barely,
With prim decorum, stirred their tea
When, through the doorway to the hall,
Bassoon and flute burst suddenly.
Aroused by music and romance,
Our rural Paris, Petushkóv,
Forsakes his tea with rum and hurries
To join with Olga in the dance.
Then Lensky calls upon Tatyána;
The poet Triquet leads Kharlikóva,
A virgin of too many years;
Buyánov whirls off Pustyakóva.
All guests are gathered in the hall
To dance or watch the brilliant ball.

40

I tried when I began my story
To conjure up (in Chapter One)
A ball at Petersburg, perhaps
The way Albani[16] might have done.
But I was for long diverted by
Vain dreams and memories, and sang
Instead the feet of lady friends.
Oh, I have lived too long awry
In tracking down their slender trails!
But since I'm through with fickle youth,
And since I'm wiser about my work
And way of life, I vow, in truth,
To keep my Chapter Five as free
From such digressions as can be.

41

Like frenzied youth in rounds unending
The waltzing couples gaily swirl;
The ballroom spins and hums with sound
While pair on pair in circles whirl.
The time of sweet revenge meanwhile
Onegin waits with secret glee:
At first he dances Olga round
The crowded ballroom, with a smile;
He makes her sit one out, to chat
Politely for a while, and then,
Two minutes later, he begins
A waltz, alone with her again.
The guests look on with blank surprise,
And Lensky can't believe his eyes.

Hi-ho! Mazurka strains resound!
The ballroom shook in days of yore
From the mazurka's mighty thud
And pounding heels upon the floor.
The jolting jarred the window-frames.
Not so these days: like gentle ladies,
We tamely glide on polished floors;
Only the countryside acclaims
Mazurka's ancient splendor fresh
And keeps the figures as of old.
There leaps and taps and stamp of heels
Remain still primitive and bold,
Mocking at fashion's tyrannies
As Russia's modern worst disease.

(43) 44

Then rude Buyánov brings Tatyána
And Olga to Onegin, who
Goes gliding off along the floor
With Olga in a dance anew;
With unconcern, at liberty,
He whispers softly in her ear
An empty compliment, his hand
Enfolding Olga's hand, while she
Glows brighter, rosier, self-pleased
From vanity and sweet elation.
But Lensky watches in his rage
And waits with jealous indignation
For the mazurka's end, his chance
To ask for the cotillion dance.

45

He's late. She cannot! No? Why not?
Onegin has the dance.—Good Lord!
She gave her word. To think she dared
To give; the girl he loved, adored
Alone from childhood days, and yet
So cunning, so deceitful now!
A child, and yet a practiced flirt!
A foolish, giddy-brained coquette!
In fury, cursing women's wiles,
He damns their tricks; he will not stay.
Poor Lensky cannot bear this blow.
He leaves the house; he rides away....
Two bullets, nothing more, and straight
The duel shall decide his fate.

Chapter Six

Là, sotto i giorni nubilosi e brevi,
Nasce una gente a cui l'morir non dole.

Petrarch

I

On finding that his friend had left,
Onegin, still at Olga's side,
Sat sulking, bored beyond endurance,
Yet with his vengeance satisfied.
And Olga, also bored, likewise
Began to yawn; the long cotillion
Seemed weary like a heavy dream.
She searched for Lensky with her eyes.
The dance had ended. After supper,
A bed was found for every guest
In rooms and halls up to the attic.
Each one was glad for quiet rest
And sleep. Onegin to his own
Estate rode off, to be alone.

2

Past midnight. In the drawing-room
Snored loud the heavy Pustyakóv
Beside his portly better half.
Gvozdín, Buyánov, Petushkóv,
And Flyánov, who was indisposed,
Were bedded in the dining-room
On chairs. Monsieur Triquet, in cap
And flannels, in the hallway dozed.
In Olga's and Tatyána's rooms
The girls lay fast asleep. Beside
The window-sill in clear moonlight
Tatyána sat alone, and sighed.
She tried to sleep, but all in vain;
She gazed upon the darkened plain.

3

Onegin's unforeseen appearance,
His momentary tender glance,
And then his manner, the attention
He gave to Olga at the dance,
Alarmed and hurt her inwardly.
His strange behavior troubled her;
She felt as though an icy hand
Had wrung her heart in jealousy,
As though a rumbling black abyss
Lay gaping now beneath her feet.
"I'll be undone," Tatyána murmured,
"But ruin at his hands is sweet.
Why rail at Fate's decree? I guess
He cannot give me happiness."

4

But I must hasten to present
A name essential to my plan.
About four miles or so away
From Lensky's manor, lives a man
Who thrives this moment as I write,—
A rowdy, once a daring bully,
Zarétsky, chief of gaming tables,
Well known as a blatherskite
Among the tavern hangers-on.
He's now a worthy family head,
A friend dependable in trouble,
A prudent squire, and though unwed,
An honest fellow, if you please.
Our age grows better by degrees.

5

There was a time when flatterers
His ruffian daring ways approved,
And true enough, his pistol-shot
An ace at fifteen paces proved.
And let it be remembered, too,
That in the heat of Eighteen Twelve
He made his mark by falling off
His horse, dead drunk. He rolled into
A ditch, and, captured by the French,
Became the prize of their campaign.
This modern Regulus of honor
Would suffer foreign chains again
If he might drink each day his fill
At Very's[1] place on credit still.

6

Time was he loved to joke and tease,
The simpletons to mortify,
Or mock the wiser for his sport
Quite openly or on the sly;
And yet sometimes his raillery
And jests had cost him very dear
And often got him into scrapes,
Like any dupe through trickery.
He took delight in long disputes
With clever or obtuse replies;
He shrewdly scoffed, but shrewdly too
He held his peace if that seemed wise.
He'd bring two friends by wiles and spite
Upon the duel grounds to fight,

7

Or reconcile old friends again
And share a dinner set for three,
Yet later slander them in secret
With lies or jesting pleasantry.
Sed alia tempora! To youth
Alone belong such pranks and daring
(Like dreams of love, another folly).
But now Zarétsky was in truth,
Like sage Horatius, pleased to live
Beneath birdcherries and pea-trees,
Secluded from the stormy world,
And plant his cabbages at peace,
Content his geese and ducks to breed
And teach his children how to read.

8

No fool was he; although Onegin
Doubted his excellence of heart,
He liked him for his common sense
And judgments, often keen and smart.
He liked, in fact, to have him call
To chat of this and that at leisure.
Hence, when he called next day, Onegin
Did not appear surprised at all.
Zarétsky, after he was greeted,
Before their chat could well begin,
At once the message from the poet
Presented with a knowing grin.
Onegin to the window drew
And read the note in silence through.

9

It was a dignified brief letter,
Polite in wording to the end:
With cold resolve the poet called
For satisfaction from his friend.
Onegin did not hesitate,
And turning quickly to the envoy,
He answered he was 'always ready.'
As though he did not care to wait,
Zarétsky rose; he took no time
For explanations or delay,
But left, declaring that he had
A lot of work at home. All day
Onegin was oppressed by shame
And could not rid himself of blame.

10

At heart, Onegin with good reason
Now freely judged in privacy
That he was from the outset wrong.
He blamed himself when, heedlessly,
The night before he had been seen
To mock their tender, shy first love;
Besides, one should forgive a youth
Who is in love at age eighteen
And give him leave to play the fool.
Onegin liked his friend. He might
Have shown true tolerance and not
A childish readiness to fight;
He might have proved his common sense
And curbed the feeling of offense;

11

He might have shown his finer nature
Instead of bristling like a beast;
He might have undeceived the youth
With plain, disarming words at least.
"Too late! There's nothing now I dare
Undo," he thought instead; "besides,
That meddling duelist, that fierce
Old gossip shares in this affair.
It's best, of course, to disregard
His scorn, but then men's jeering loud,
Sly whispers, fools' contempt!" Alas,
The stupid judgment of the crowd![2]
Thus honor like a god now rules
And makes of men its willing tools.

12

At home, the poet fumed with hatred,
Impatient for his just redress.
At last his babbling messenger
Returned, exulting in success.
The jealous lover's now at rest—
Delighted! He had feared the rogue
Might try some subterfuge or guile,
Or treat the matter as a jest
To save his skin by some pretense.
But now his doubts were gone, and they
Would meet tomorrow by the mill,
Tomorrow, at the break of day,
And there the pistol-shots let fly
Each at the other's head or thigh.

13

Still angry and resolved to hate
His Olga, Lensky would not see
That cruel flirt before the duel.
He marked the hours, but finally,
Despite his vow, his charge of blame,
He found himself inside her gates.
He thought his coming would confuse
The flirt and make her hide in shame.
How wrong he was! Swift down the steps
On twinkling feet his Olga ran,
Like hope, moved by its own sweet will,
To meet him—that unhappy man—
As glad, as gay and free, the way
She'd run on any other day.

"Last night you left us in a hurry,"
In her elation Olga said.
Poor Lensky faltered, at a loss
For words, then simply hung his head.
His rancor and his jealousy
Had fled before her radiance,
Her girlish tenderness, her joy,
Her open, dear simplicity!
Then, feeling he was still beloved,
He looked at her, by rapture stirred,
And, suffering remorse, he yearned
To ask forgiveness. In a word,
He felt his jealous fears were vain,
And all was well for him again.

(15, 16) 17

Then Lensky, growing sorrowful
Because of Olga's sweet delight,
Had not the courage to discuss
What happened at the dance last night.
He thought: "I'll save her presently!
I won't permit that libertine
To turn with flattery and sighs
Her youthful heart away from me;
I won't allow a worm so vile
To eat the lily's stem away,
Nor watch the flower fade before
It blooms—the bud of just one day."
Such feelings moved him in the end
To fight the duel with his friend.

18

Had he but known the burning hurt
That filled poor Tanya's heart of woe!
Had Tanya only guessed their hate
In time, or had she come to know
About the duel between the two
Good friends at dawn for life or death,
She might have reunited them
As love alone has power to do!
But not a soul has yet surmised
Or seemed to understand her passion
And secret sorrow, since Onegin
Remained aloof as was his fashion.
Her nanny might have guessed and told,
But she was slow, so very old.

19

All evening Lensky was distracted:
Now gloomy, silent, then too gay;
But poets, nurselings of the Muses,
Are always thus. He'd start to play
The clavichord with frowning brow
But struck some single chords alone
And stopped. Then, glancing up to Olga,
Cried, "Ah, we're happy anyhow!
Not so?" The hour grew late; 'twas time
To say goodbye. He felt his heart
Would almost break with pain on leaving,
With silent grieving torn apart.
She asked: "What's wrong with you today?"
"Nothing!" He turned and rode away.

20

At home he took his pistols out,
Examined them and boxed them right,
And then, undressing, opened Schiller
To read in bed by candle-light.
But steadily one mournful thought
Haunted his mind: he saw his Olga
Unutterably dear and fair
And always near. In vain he sought
The printed page; he closed the book.
Inspired by tender ecstasy
And love's extravagance and folly,
He wrote a poem, sincere and free,
Then read, entranced, his lyric lines
Like Delvig[3] drunk each time he dines.

21

I have his poem, by loving hands
Preserved somehow from perishing:
"Ah, whither, whither have you vanished,
My youth, my golden days of spring?
What promise? What my destiny?
In vain my glances probe the dark
Profound and seek to know my fate
Within the living mystery.
The fates are just. Perhaps the flame
Will pass me by, or pierce my breast;
Then mine the hour of waking life
Or mine the everlasting rest.
Blessed the day of toil and light!
Blessed the coming of the night!

"Wake up! Onegin's waiting there!
It's after six! No time to spare!"

22

"Another day will dawn tomorrow;
Another day will shine in light
When I shall pass among the shadows
In the unfathomable night.
Another poet's memory
Will sink in Lethe's sluggish tide.
The world will soon forget. Will you,
My Best, will you remember me?
O vision beautiful and true,
Will you not sorrow where I lie,
And muse: 'He vowed his stormy youth
And love to me,—one soon to die!'
O dearest, come! I cry to you!
O come, my bride, forever true."[4]

23

That *vague* and *languid* style is called
Romantic (though I do not find
One feature of romantic passion
In what he wrote.[5] But never mind!)
At last, near dawn, his heavy head
Began to droop from weariness
Above the fashionable word
Ideal. Then Lensky drowsed in bed.
But when in deep forgetfulness
He fell asleep, his second came
Into his still, secluded study
And called him loudly by his name:
"Wake up! Onegin's waiting there!
It's after six! No time to spare!"

24

But he was wrong in that. Onegin
Was dead asleep. Although afar
The shades of night were growing thinner
And cocks had hailed the morning star,
Onegin still lay sound asleep.
The sun had long since mounted high;
A snowstorm, whirling, drifted past
In crystal light; he slumbered deep
And long, insensible, at peace.
Aroused at last, he drew aside
The curtains drowsily, in wonder
About the time of day outside,
And then remembered with dismay
He must be up without delay.

25

He rings the bell. His serving-man
Comes running in, Monsieur Guillot,
Bringing his slippers, dressing-gown,
And change of linen, white as snow.
Onegin dresses in the space
Of minutes. He tells Guillot to be
Prepared to drive along with him
At once and bring the pistol-case.
The sleigh is waiting at the door.
Off to the water-mill they tear
Away to reach the duel grounds.
Arrived, he bids his servant bear
Lepage's[6] deadly arms, then tie
The horses to an oak nearby.

26

There Lensky waited with impatience
Above the mill-dam, forced to hear
Zarétsky's views on mills and boasts
Of being a homebred engineer.
With apologies Onegin came.
Zarétsky in amazement cried:
"But, Sir, your second? Where is he?"
A duelist of the classic frame
Of mind, precise about the rules
And code of honor,[7] pointedly
He disapproved of careless killing
And held to keeping formally
The good traditional old ways—
A bias well deserving praise.

27

"My second?" queried then Onegin.
"He's here, my friend, Monsieur Guillot.
I'm sure you hardly would refuse
The man I bring with me. Although
He's little known, he is at heart
A fine old chap." Zarétsky chewed
His lips in wrath. Onegin then
Called out to Lensky: "Shall we start?
And Lensky answered: "As you please.
I'm ready." Slowly then the two
Walked to the mill. And while the seconds
In earnest hastened to review
Their plans, by regulations bound,
The foes stood staring at the ground.

28

Foes!—How long had they been parted
As friends by their revengeful mood?
How long since they together shared
Their leisure, secrets, wine, and food
In quiet company? But now,
As two hereditary foes,
As victims of a senseless dream,
They coldly scheme and fiercely vow
Eternal hatred, sudden death. . . .
Could they but laugh again at ease
Before their hands are stained with blood,
And, reconciled, go home in peace!—
But worldly hate, like worldly fame,
Shrinks at the breath of worldly shame.

29

The shining pistols are uncased;
The hammers ring on ramrods; quick
Inside the polished barrels now
The bullets slide; the triggers click.
Grey powder's sifted carefully
Into the pans. The pointed flints,
Screwed safely in, are set again.
In his alarm, behind a tree
Guillot stands watching, puzzled by
The strange event. The rivals drop
Their cloaks. Then two and thirty steps
Zarétsky paces to a stop;
He takes each rival to his stand,
Each with a pistol in his hand.

30

"And now, advance!"
                    Relentless, calm,
The foes, as yet not taking aim,
With steady step, unhurried, slow,
Across the snow four paces came,
Four fateful paces closer to
Their death. Onegin was the first
To raise his weapon slowly while
Advancing. Five steps more the two
Came, resolute. Then screwing up
His left eye, Lensky too began
To aim. But even at that moment
Onegin fired. . . . Unhappy man,
How brief his hour! Without a sound,
His pistol dropped upon the ground,

31

His fingers clutching at his breast,
The poet fell. His clouded eyes
The secret agony of death
Alone revealed. Thus tumbling flies
An avalanche of sheeted snow
And falls while sparkling in the sun
Below the mountainside from sight.
Onegin sank with horror, low
Beside his friend there lying dead
In snow. His friend would wake no more!
His life has ended all too soon.
A morning flower, dead before
The blasting storm, now withered lies.
The altar flame grows dim and dies.

32

He lay unmoving, strangely calm,
Like one still dreaming, numb, at rest.
His smoking blood ran from the wound;
The shot had pierced him through the breast.
A few brief moments past his heart
Was quick with living inspiration,
With hate and fears, with hope and love,
With passion, ecstasy, and art;
But now it was a house deserted,
All dark and still, the shutters tight,
The windows bleak and bleared with chalk,
The host departed in the night.
Where to? God knows. . . . Here not a trace
Remained to tell his dwelling place.

33

'Tis pleasant with a spiteful sally
To madden an unwary foe,
To see him lower sullenly
His stubborn head against the blow;
Or watch when, willy-nilly, he
Beholds his shame as in a glass;
Or even hear the arrant dullard
Bellow aloud, "It looks like me!"
'Tis sweeter yet to wish in silence
His honorable death, instead,
And hope that at the usual range
He'll get a bullet in his head.
But outright killing by a plan
Can hardly please an honest man.

34

Suppose your pistol shot had killed
By chance a dear and youthful friend
Because of some annoying look
Or trifling word that did offend
Your honor while you sat at wine?
Suppose that in a blaze of anger
He called you proudly to a fight?
What feelings would possess your fine
High-spirited, disdainful soul
When in a moment you behold
Him lying under seal of death
And see him slowly growing cold?
When dumb in boundless dark he lies,
Stone-deaf to your despairing cries?

35

Gripping the pistol in his hand
With passionate remorse and dread,
Onegin, blinded, stood. He heard
His neighbor's verdict: "Well, he's dead."
Dead! . . . At this fearful affirmation,
Onegin, shuddering and crushed,
Ran quick to call for aid. Zarétsky,
With gentle care and veneration
For one they'd treasured as a friend
Arranged the body in the sleigh.
Scenting the dead, the panting horses
Began to snort and rear away;
Champing their steely bits in foam,
They swiftly sped, like arrows, home.

36

O friends! You, too, lament the poet:
One young and happy in his mind,
With little in his life accomplished,
His boyhood scarcely left behind,
He perished. Say, his ardor, where?
Where now his song, his aspirations,
His passion and his noble feeling—
So tender, resolute, so fair?
Where thirst for knowledge, work and fame?
And where his longing after love,
His dread of shame and all things base?
And where his dream of life above
Our world of things we know and see?
O dreams of sacred poetry!

37

Perhaps the youth was born to bless
Mankind, or win at least renown,
And thus his silenced lyre would have
In mighty strains resounded down
The centuries forevermore.
Perhaps a place of honor great
Awaited him among mankind;
Perhaps his martyred spirit bore
Away into the grave a truth
Divine, a sacred mystery,
A living voice to make the world
Rejoice,—now in eternity
His soul denied to hear the fame
And praise we sing unto his name.

(38) 39

Perhaps an humbler destiny
The poet might have known in life,
Fated too soon to waste his youth
And eagerness in daily strife.
He might have changed in many ways,
Abandoned poetry, and lazed
In a quilted robe, horned, or loved
A faithful wife for all his days.
He might have placed his trust in facts;
At forty might have had the gout,
Content to eat, to drink, to mope,
As he grew flabby, old, and stout,
And in the end, surrounded by
His children, wife and kin, to die.

40

Whate'er his future might have held,
The youthful lover met his end,—
The poet and the pensive dreamer
Slain in a duel by his friend!
There is a quiet spot near where
The one beloved of Muses lived:
Two fir trees twine their tangled roots
Above a brook slow winding there
To meet the stream far down the valley.
Where plowmen love to rest beside
The brook, where girls at reaping plunge
Their ringing pitchers in the tide,
A simple monument of stone
Above the valley rises lone.

41

And here, when springtime showers fall
On greening fields, and winter's past,
The shepherd chants of Volga fishers
And plaits himself his shoes of bast.
Sometimes a city lass, well known,
Spending a summer in the country
Rides by on horseback, galloping
Across the meadowland alone.
She lingers for a moment here
Beside the tomb, her gauzy veil
Brushed back, to read the little legend
On the gravestone, the simple tale
Too briefly told,—and tears will rise
To dim with grief her tender eyes.

42

Then slowly, plunged in reverie,
Long through the country she will ride,
With Lensky's fate her wistful spirit,
Despite herself, pre-occupied,
And wonder: "Where is Olga? How
Her loss she suffered, and how long?
How soon her tears of sorrow dried?
And where's her older sister now?
And he, that gloomy solitary,
Who grimly fled society,
That modish foe of modish belles,
The poet's slayer, where is he?"
Another day I shall not fail
To answer all in each detail,

43

But not today. I hold my hero
In warm affection and I vow
To tell his story somewhat later,
But such is not my purpose now.
Stern prose demands my care and time,
And I confess that, at my age,
I court the Muse begrudgingly
And scorn the waywardness of rhyme.
No more I find it as delightful
To mar long pages as of old,
For sterner cares and sterner duties
More steadfast I today behold;
In crowded halls or solitude
They haunt my soul and dreamy mood.

44

I live with truer aspirations,
Aware of sorrows new that fret
My heart, and though deluded often,
My oldtime griefs I still regret.
Where, where my ecstasies of youth?
And are my laurels faded now,
(To use one more romantic rhyme)
Are my illusions fled, forsooth?
And is it now indeed a fact
As I in jest have often said,
All elegiac words aside,
My springtime days of life are dead?
Shall I be really thirty soon
And far beyond my hour of noon?

Shall I be really thirty soon
And far beyond my hour of noon?

45

My afternoon of life has come.
I must accept the painful truth.
So fare you well, my oldtime friends!
So fare you well, my merry youth!
My gratitude for days of strife,
For torments tender, days of gladness,
For hours of sadness, feasts of wine!
For every gift and good of life,
My thanks once more. Alike in peace
And wild alarm I found delight;
I've had my fill. I am content. . . .
Enough! My soul is calm tonight:
I long to live on sunlit ways
And put aside my yesterdays.

46

One parting glance again. Farewell,
Dear refuge in my wilderness,
Where, lulled in quiet contemplation,
I mused for long in idleness.
And you, O youthful inspiration,
Awake anew my dreamy spirit!
Come often to my solitude
To rouse the poet's imagination!
Oh, do not let my spirit turn
To stone, insensible at heart,
Grow hard and cruel, cold to men,
Intemperate in every part,—
And sink in pools of social muck,
Dear friends, where you and I are stuck.

Chapter Seven

O Moscow, Russia's dearest child!
Where is thy equal to be found?
Dmitriev

Our Moscow, who could fail to love thee?
Baratynsky

You run down Moscow? You mocking traveler!
Where will you find a better spot?—
Yes, far away, where we are not!
Griboyédov

I

Encircled by the springtime rays,
The snow on neighbor mountains yields,
And, rioting, the turbid freshets
Sweep down and flood the level fields.
Bluer each day the heavens gleam;
And nature, waking, greets with smiles
And cheer the morning of the year;
The still transparent woodlands seem
To wear a delicate green down.
The bees wing from their waxen cells
Toward valleys fresh and bright with flowers
To gather tribute from the dells.
The cattle low; the nightingale
Trills in the stillness of the vale.

2

How sad for me each spring again!
O Spring, O days of love's unrest!
What languor fills my soul, what vague
Emotions stir within my breast
When in a quiet greenwood place,
With yearning in my troubled blood,
I feel your soft celestial light
And breezes blowing in my face!
Am I from springtime joy estranged,
From tides of glory and delight,
From gifts of happiness and song?
Shall I then languish in the night
Fast gathering about my bed—
With anguish and with boredom dead?

3

Or do we grieve the fall of leaves
Long doomed to die, and mourn in vain
Their loss at each recurring spring,
When all the world is gay again?
Or Nature's season of rebirth
Would we with faded years long dead
Compare, then brood forever on
Man's unreturning days on earth?
Perhaps some long forgotten springtime
Comes soundless back,—a vanished gleam
Of happiness in trembling light,—
And, soaring in a lyric dream,
We long to feel a far-off boon,
A night of magic, and a moon. . . .

How sad for me each spring again!
O Spring, O days of love's unrest!

181

4

Well, spring is here! You idlers, drones,
Wise men, you epicures in taste,
You carefree sons, you fellows true
To Levshin's[1] principles, make haste!
You Priams of the rural places
And gentlewomen sentimental,
Spring calls you to a countryside
Of sunshine, flowers, open spaces,
Surprising drives, and pleasant walks
In the bewitching starry night.
Then hurry, hurry to the fields
In crowded stage, or else go light
By post, by cart of any kind!
Come, leave the city gates behind!

5

You also, my indulgent reader,
In your imported carriage, leave
The great unresting town, your home
Of winter joy and make-believe.
Come with my wayward Muse to hear
The rustling of the forest trees
Along the nameless river where
Onegin, through the winter year,
Lived in his country seat of late
In idleness, in sad seclusion,
A neighbor to my dear Tatyána,
My maid of fancy and illusion.
His house is vacant, yet we find
He left a trail of grief behind.

6

Within a hill-encircled valley
We'll follow by a brook that flows
Among the greening fields to meet
A river where the linden grows.
There wild the rose and briars bloom;
There sings all night the nightingale
And murmurs soft a silver spring.
And, too, there lies a granite tomb
Between two venerable pines.
The legend tells the passer-by
On graven stone the name and age:
Vladimir Lensky here doth lie
Who early died as die the brave.
Repose, O Poet, in thy grave!

7

There was a time the morning breeze
Moved to and fro a lonely wreath
Hung on a sagging pine-tree bough
Above the humble urn of death.
Here two young women often came
Within the gathered dark of night
To sit in moonlight arm in arm
And mourn one dear remembered name.
But now the lonely tomb is long
Forgot. The trail lies overgrown
In weeds. No wreath hangs on the bough.
A frail old shepherd sits alone
Beneath that pine as in the past
And, humming, weaves his shoes of bast.

Poor Lensky! No, she did not pine
In sorrow long; her tears were brief.
His bride-to-be a little while
Continued faithful in her grief.
Another lured her youthful heart;
Another captured her attention
And found a way to change her mind
By flattery and lover's art.[2]
A lancer pleased, a lancer charmed
Her heart. And soon, with head bent down
Before the altar bashfully,
She wore a bridal veil and crown,
Her lowered eyes aglow, the while
Her lips were parted in a smile.

11

Poor Lensky! Past the bounds of death
In regions of eternity,
Was he, the mournful poet, troubled
By Olga's fateful perfidy?
Or, lulled by Lethe in his rest,
Rejoicing in forgetfulness,
Was he unmoved, from all the world
Estranged, set free, forever blest?
Ah, yes! when life is past, complete
Oblivion is awaiting us:
No friend, no foe, no lover's voice
Survives. Alone the angry chorus
Of heirs indecently will rage
While wrangling o'er the heritage.

12

Soon Olga's voice no more was heard
In her own family. She went
Because her lancer, slave of duty,
Was ordered to his regiment.
Her frail old mother in her grief
Wept bitterly. Distraught with pain,
She came to tell her child godspeed;
But Tanya could not find relief
In tears; her mournful face grew pale
With deathlike pallor. When at last
They crowded near the porch or drew
Beside the carriage-door, downcast,
Tatyána too came out, and nigh
The couple stood, to say goodbye.

13

A long, long time as through a mist
She watched them as they drove away.
She was alone, alone! Her friend
Of childhood years, but yesterday
Her darling gone, her little pet,
Her first and only favorite,
Now snatched away by cruel fate,
Her dearest love forever set
Apart. She wandered, aimless, through
The empty garden late at night,
But nowhere could she find true peace
Or consolation in her plight
Or ease from tears too long repressed
To still the ache within her breast.

14

Now in all her cruel loneliness
At home, Tatyána's passion burns
And to Onegin far away
Her heart impetuously turns.
She thinks she will not see his face
Again; she ought to hate the man,
Abhor him for a brother slain.
The poet perished and no trace
Of him remained in life for long.
His bride-to-be another wed;
Like smoke across the azure sky
The poet's memory had fled. . . .
Two hearts perhaps are yet forlorn
And mourn him still.—But wherefore mourn?

15

It was near dusk. The sky grew darker.
A beetle buzzed. The river flowed
In calm. Some peasant youths with song
Walked home. Beyond the river glowed
The fishers' fire. As in a sleep
Tatyána through the open meadows
Alone in silver moonlight wandered,
Alone in meditation deep.
She wandered long when suddenly
Above the hill she saw the gleam
Of manor lights, a grove of trees,
A garden-close beside a stream.
She turned, uncertain, to depart;
She felt a throbbing in her heart.

16

She stood awhile in hesitation.
"Shall I turn back? His place is near.
I'd like to see the house and garden.
I'm sure that no one knows me here."
Then, almost breathless, down the hill
Tatyána ran; she turned to look,
Perplexed in mind and undecided;
The court appeared deserted, still.
The dogs ran barking suddenly,
And at her cry a troop of boys
Came running from the huts about;
They chased the dogs away with noise
And shouts, and led with proud regard
The gentle lady through the yard.

17

"I'd like to see the manor house,"
Tatyána said, and hurriedly
The children ran to find Anísya
And ask her for the front-door key.
Anísya quickly came to show
The lady at the entrance-door
The empty house. Then Tanya saw
The study where not long ago
Her hero dwelt alone: there lay
A billiard cue on the table top;
Upon the littered sofa, long
Forgotten, lay a riding-crop.
"At this hearth," mumbled the old crone,
"My master always sat alone.

18

"My master and our neighbor Lensky
Here often used to dine together.
Please follow me. I'll show you now
My master's room. In winter weather
He liked it best of all; he took
His coffee here, received the bailiff
Daily or read the morning through. . . .
The old master also loved this nook:
Beside the window here, on Sundays,
He'd put his glasses on and play
A game of cards with me to pass
An evening pleasantly. And may
God keep his soul among the blest
And grant his soul eternal rest."

19

With loving tenderness Tatyána
Looked all about her. Everything
She saw appeared a precious treasure
That comforted her suffering,
Half-soothèd and excited heart;
The lamp unlighted on the table,
A pile of books, the bed and rug
Beneath the window-sill apart,
The view into the moonlit night
In pale half-light of violet,
Lord Byron's portrait on the wall
And the little iron statuette
With folded arms—familiar now,—
Cocked hat and melancholy brow.

20

Long in this modern hermit's cell
Tatyána, as if enchanted, stood.
The hour grew late. The wind blew colder
Across the valley floor. The wood
And river lay in mist and gloom.
The moon went down behind a hill
And far too soon the hour had come
When our fair pilgrim should go home.
Though Tanya hid her agitation,
'Twas not without a sigh of pain
She started home. She pleaded first
To be allowed to come again
To this secluded house alone
And read some books to her unknown.

21

She took her leave outside the gate
And bade the housekeeper goodbye.
She came back to the manor house
Next day before the sun was high.
And, in the silent study there,
Forgetting all the world outside,
She found herself at last alone
And long she wept in her despair.
But soon the books absorbed her mind.
They seemed beyond her range and need
At first; she thought the volumes strange,
Too modern. She began to read,
Her soul athirst to understand,
And found a world unknown at hand.

22

Although Onegin in his boredom
Disliked most authors to a man,
There were a certain few he favored
And had excluded from his ban:
Such were *Don Juan* and *The Giaour,*
Two, three contemporary novels[3]
In which he found the modern era
And human beings of the hour
Described with some degree of truth,—
Unprincipled, immoral, vain,
Inordinately visionary,
Self-seeking, sterile with disdain,
With their embittered minds at sea
Seething in vain activity.

23

Here many pages showed the sharp
Impressions of his finger-nail;
And all these signs attentively
Tatyána noted without fail.
She noted, scanned in trepidation
What passages had struck his mind,
The lines that held his acquiescence
In meaning, thought, or observation;
She scanned the margins he had scored
With pencil-marks, and she found there
Unconsciously himself revealing,
Onegin had his soul laid bare
By crosses, queries terse and stark,
Or a sharp interrogation mark.

24

Thus step by step my Tanya then
Began to understand, to see
More clearly, God be praised, the man
Whom she by fate's most stern decree
Had come through suffering to love:
Was he a man to fear? a freak?[4]
Spirit of Heaven or of Hell?
Proud demon? angel from above?
Who was this man? A sorry phantom,
An empty echo, an imitation?
A Russian posing as Childe Harold?
A man of whims, the incarnation
Of every modernistic rage,
Or a parody upon his age?

25

Had she the answer to the riddle,
Had she *the word*, the special key?
The hours went by; she had forgotten
At home the waiting family,
Where even now two neighbors met
Were talking at this time about her.
"What can I do? She's not a child,"
Her mother groaned. "Not married, yet!
It's time Tatyána should be settled
For she's the older of the two.
But, heavens, she refuses all
Her suitors,—what am I to do?
She answers 'No!' She mopes and roves
Alone among the fields and groves."

26

"Is she in love perhaps?" "With whom,
I wonder? Buyánov she refused
Outright; the same with Petushkóv.
Our guest hussar Pykhtín then used
All sorts of wooing tricks. I thought
He genuinely loved Tatyána
And that she would at last consent,
But did she? Bah! It came to naught."
"My dear, you'd better take her straight
To Moscow. That's the place to go!
That is the market-place for brides."
"The cost! My income is too low."
"One winter would suffice. Indeed,
I'll gladly lend the cash you need."

27

The good old lady was delighted
With this advice, so full of reason,
And fell to reckoning expenses
For going in the winter season.
Tatyána heard the news with fear:
To face a stern exacting world
In judgment there upon her shy
Provincial ways, then to appear
In long outmoded dowdy dress;
To use her common simple style
Of country speech before those belles
And beaus, and bear a mocking smile!—
Oh, horrors! Better far away
Among the groves and meadows stay.

28

She rises with the early light,
At dawn. In haste Tatyána flies
Into the fields to look about her
With tender sorrow in her eyes:
"Farewell to you, my woodland grove,
And you, familiar peaceful valleys,
And you, my sunny hills! Farewell
To skies and loveliness above,
To all of nature calm with joy!
For sheer pretense and brilliancy
I leave the haunts of light and peace,
My quiet home, my liberty!
And whither? To what alien shore?
What next has fate for me in store?"

29

Her walks are ever longer, slower
Beside each brook, upon each knoll,
With rambling and with lingering
Enchanted deep within her soul.
She runs to all the fields that lie
About her, every field and grove,
To hear them speak to her again!
But summer passes swiftly by.
Then autumn comes in dress of gold
When Nature, paler, trembling, grieves
Like a sacrifice in bright array. . . .
The cold winds bellow, driving leaves
Across the meadows far and near,
And, lo! our fairy Winter's here!

Her walks are ever longer, slower
Beside each brook, upon each knoll

194

30

She comes in whirls, her tresses twined
In tufts on oak-tree bough and bole;
Her billowy soft carpets lie
Upon the fields, adown each knoll.
The leveled banks and peaceful streams
Sleep under eider-down white shrouds.
The hoar-frost glows, and we rejoice
In Winter's gay fantastic dreams.
But only Tanya feels her grief
And great distress. She does not go
Outside to sniff the winter cold,
To wash her neck and face with snow
And taste the winter's frosty nip.
Tatyána dreads the winter trip.

31

The day of leaving was for long
Delayed, but now the hour is due.
The long-neglected sleigh is well
Inspected, mended, lined anew.
They have the usual baggage-train
Of three large sledges heaped with goods:
Trunks, boxes, mattresses, and chairs,
Pots, basins, hen coops, hay and grain,
Jars of jellies, all sorts of pans,
Some feather pillows, bowls and pails,
Et cetera,—a world of things.
The servants come with parting wails
Midst weeping loud of household maids;
The men lead out the eighteen jades,

32

And, while the cooks prepare the breakfast,
They're hitched up to the master's sleigh;
The cooks and drivers shout and swear;
The heavy sledges creak and sway.
The bearded post-boy mounts astride
His lean old nag. The serfs and servants
Now bid the ladies all goodbye
And crowd the gate on every side.
All's ready now! . . . The heavy sleigh
Slides slowly, safely through the gate.
"Farewell, my solitary home!
Farewell, my youth, my peace of late!
My refuge of these many years!"
Tatyána can't restrain her tears.

33

When we extend the benefits
And bounds of culture, we will bring
In time (five hundred years henceforth
By scientific reckoning)
Improvements in the highways quite
Beyond our boldest calculations:
A net of highways will connect
Points far and near, to left and right;
Huge iron bridges then will span
With arcs the waters; we shall part
The mountains, dig neath river-beds,
Cut tunnels by our craft and art,
And put up pleasant inns to boot
At every station on the route.

34

But now our roads are horrible:
The bridges rot in disrepair;
At every station bugs and fleas
Drive travelers to sheer despair.
We have no inns. Instead,—the blight
Of barren, draughty huts with old
Pretentious menus hung for show,
In gloom, to mock the appetite.
Meantime before their sluggish fires
The cyclops of our rural parts
Labor to mend with hammer-blows
The light-wheeled craft of Western marts,
Grateful for all the ruts on hand
And ditches of the fatherland.

35

But, in the winter time, our trips
Are too delightful to seem long;
The highways then are light and smooth
As verses in a modern song.
The coachman is alert behind
The swift, unweary troika team,
And mileposts flash like palings by,
Delighting the beholder's mind.
But Tanya's mother feared the cost
Of post expense, and so she went
By stages with her many teams.
Thus Tanya had her heart's content
Of boredom through the country ways.
Their journey lasted seven days.

36

The goal is near at last. Before them
White Moscow lifts her crosses high
Above her ancient domes of gold,
Ablaze with splendor in the sky.
How great my joy, my friends, to see
The churches with their belfries, towers,
The gardens, palace-halls, and spires
Leap up before me suddenly!
In bitter exile wandering,
How often, grieved by separation,
O Moscow, have I longed for thee,
Aroused in my imagination!
Moscow! ... That holy word can start
A tumult in each Russian heart.

37

There Peter's Palace rises grim
In pride among the ancient trees,
All stern with memories of fame.[5]
Elated by his victories,
Napoleon waited here in vain
For Moscow, kneeling at his feet,
To tender him the Kremlin keys.
But never did my Moscow deign
To stoop with bended head in shame
With gifts before the conqueror;
But she set off a conflagration
To stay the impatient lord of war.
Deep sunk in gloom, he saw the rise
Of doom ablaze across the skies.

38

Goodbye, proud Palace, witness of
His fallen glory! . . . On, on, to greet
The capital! The city gates
Gleam white. And here's Tverskáya Street.
Their sleighs run bumping over ruts.
They flash by sentry-boxes, carts,
By market stalls, old women, gardens,
Sleighs, lamp-posts, monasteries, huts,
A palace, fashionable shops,
Stone balconies, a boulevard,
Great mansions, Cossacks, pharmacies,
Fat merchants, boys, police on guard,
The gates with lions' stony jaws,[6]
And crosses black with flocks of daws.

(39) 40

For near two hours through city streets
Their weary baggage-train had passed
When at a gate by St. Khariton,
Off in a narrow lane, at last
They stopped. Here lived an oldtime kin,
A frail consumptive aunt, for four
Long years unwell. A grey Kalmuk
With spectacles, attired in
An old caftan, and holding a sock
Half-mended in his hand, threw wide
The entrance-door. The princess cried
Her greeting from a room inside.
The cousins, after many years,
Embraced with kisses, cries, and tears.

41

"Princess, *mon ange!*" "Pachette!" "Aline!"
"How wonderful!" "How long it seems!"
"You'll stay, I hope? *Cousine!* My darling!
Sit down! It's like the best of dreams!
It's like a novel now come true!"
"And here's my eldest child—my Tanya."
"Ah, Tanya dear, come here to me.—
I must be dreaming. . . . Now you do
Remember Grandison, of course?"
"What Grandison? . . . Oh, Grandison!
Of course I do. And where's he now?"
"In Moscow, here, by St Simeon.
He called on me on Christmas Eve.
His son is married, I believe.

42

"We'll talk of him another time—
Tomorrow! Good? And we must show
Off Tanya to the family.
Myself, I am too weak to go;
I hardly drag about at best. . . .
But come, you must be really tired,
And need, like me, a little time
For resting. . . . Ah, again, my chest!
The pains. . . . A grain of joy feels like
A burden always to endure. . . .
The vilest thing there is—old age!
I'm good for nothing, to be sure."
But feeling weak, she then broke off
And ended in a racking cough.

43

Her sick aunt's joy and tenderness
Had touched Tatyána; accustomed still
To her own quiet room at home,
She found herself depressed and ill
At ease. Behind the silken curtain
Of her strange bed, when church-bells tolled
The rising hour of care and labor,
She lay unrested and uncertain,
Aroused too soon, or in the darkness
Sat near the narrow window-pane.
But in the murky chill at dawn
She saw no meadow, grove, or plain;
She saw but fences running round
The cook-house, yard, and stable-ground.

44

Each day there was a dinner party
In style, for Tanya to be viewed
By grandmammas attracted by
Her air of pensive lassitude.
With gracious hospitality
At every home the kinsfolk asked
Their country visitors for dinner.
"How Tanya's grown! It seems to me
I stood godmother yesterday!"
"I dandled you, my baby dear!"
"I gave you cakes and gingerbread."
"Why, yes, I used to pull your ear!"
And grandmammas in chorus sigh:
"Good heavens, how the years do fly!"

45

They do not change. Year after year
They keep their old familiar ways:
Old aunt Yeléna wears the bonnet
Of tulle she wore in other days;
Lukérya Lvóvna paints; *cousine*
Lyubóv Petróvna fibs as ever;
Iván Petróvich is still a dunce;
His older brother still plain mean.
Aunt Pelagéya still possesses
Monsieur Finemouche, her ancient flame,
Her spitz, and too her gentle spouse
Who's still as humble, still the same
Good clubman, faithful, deaf, but who
Still eats and drinks enough for two.

46

Their daughters, after brief embraces,
Observe Tatyána silently
From head to foot. The Moscow Graces
In their youthful partiality
Decide their cousin's colorless,
Provincial, odd, somewhat affected,
A trifle pale, a trifle thin,
Demure, attractive more or less.
Then quickly they become her dear,
Dear friends; they take her up to stay
With them; they squeeze her tenderly,
Fluff up her hair the latest way,
And gaily share, with girlish art
Their little secrets of the heart,

47

Their hopes and dreams, their girlish pranks,
A friend's small triumph or their own.
With bits of guile and harmless slander
They gossip in a singsong tone,
But seek, for all their confidence
And chatter, in return to hear
Tatyána's fondest hopes revealed.
But she, in her indifference,
Appears as in a dreamlike state;
She listens with a careless smile
Half absently to what is said,
And guards inviolate the while
The secret of her heart, her fears,
Her source of happiness and tears.

48

Tatyána really longed to learn
Their way of life, their conversation;
Instead she heard in drawing-rooms
Mere chatter, empty animation,
Mere callous, incoherent, stale,
Vain talk where even slander seemed
A dull affair. In all their world
Of news, small talk, and tattle-tale,
She found no gleam of any wit,
No hint of searching thought, no smart
Retort, no word at random spoken
To stir the mind or thrill the heart;
No jest nor satire in their chaff,
No plain good fun to make one laugh.

49

A group of youthful archivists[7]
Once at a brilliant masquerade
Described her in their self-conceit
As just an awkward country maid.
One wag assumed she was a tame
Sweet girl, ideal in a sense,
And boasted, leaning in the doorway,
He'd write a poem to her name.
But wise Prince Vyázemsky,[8] who met
Her at his aunt's, sat down beside her,
And touched her depth of mind and soul.
Then one old nobleman espied her,
Asked gravely who she was, and took
The pains to straighten his peruke.

50

But where Melpomene[9] speaks long
And loud with moving eloquence
And waves her tinseled scarf before
A sluggish, heedless audience;
Where gentle Thalia may drowse,
Indifferent to friendly clapping;
Where for Terpsichore alone
Her young admirers crowd the house
(As was the case with you and me
In our forgotten younger days),
She was unnoticed. At no box
Or stall did jealous ladies raise
Lorgnettes to watch Tatyána pass;
Or connoisseurs, the opera glass.

Prince Vyázemsky sat down beside her

They drive her to the Nobles' Club.
The stuffy, crowded halls, the roar,
The blaring band, the glare of candles,
The couples whirling on the floor,
The throngs that crowd the gallery,
The groups of hopeful brides-to-be
And beauties in their filmy dresses,
Confound the senses suddenly.
Here errant dandies of the season
Show off with impudence their gay
Waistcoats, lorgnettes, and brazen airs.
Hussars on leave in fine array
Come, dashing, for a moment here—
To glitter, conquer, disappear.

52

The night has stars exceeding bright,
And Moscow many beauties too,
Yet brighter than her night companions
The moon shines clear in azure blue.
Thus she, who means all poetry
To me, for whom I dare not hope,
Among the many wives and maidens
Shines like the moon in majesty.[10]
How graceful in her lonely pride
She walks in stateliness apart!
What languor in her magic glances!
What languor in her gentle heart! . . .
Enough, my soul! have done at last;
The follies of your youth are past.

53

Amidst the hubbub, stamping, curtsies,
Mazurkas, waltzes, quite unseen
And unobserved, Tatyána sits
Beside a column, lone, between
Two aunts and gazes absently
At dancers, dreaming to herself.
She hates the din, the stifling air,
And revelry. . . . She longs to see
Her home again, the village peasants,
Her solitary peaceful nooks,
Her flower beds, her shelf of novels,
The fields and groves, the shining brooks,
The linden-shaded avenue
Where *he* appeared in evening's blue.

54

While Tanya in her fancy dreamed
Of scenes she cherished in her heart,
A grave impressive general
Observed her steadily, apart.
The two old aunts, who, sitting near,
Were winking at each other, nudged
Tatyána's arm, and softly whispered:
"Look quickly on your left, my dear!"
"My left? But why? What's there to see?"
"No matter! Look, look anyhow!
That group of three, in front; the man
In uniform,—you see him now?
He's standing sideways. Have you seen?"
"That big fat general, you mean?"

55

I here congratulate Tatyána
Upon her catch. I pause to bring
My story back, lest I perchance
Should overlook the man I sing.
Please give me your attention now:
I sing of my young friend, and ask
The world to see his many whims.
O bless my earnest work, O thou,
My Epic Muse! Nor let me rove
Too far astray, nor let me lack
Thy faithful staff upon my way.
No more. A load is off my back:
My Invocation's done. Meanwhile,
I've paid my debt to classic style.

Chapter Eight

Fare thee well! and if for ever,
Still for ever, fare thee well.
Byron

I

When still at school in the Lyceum
I lived at ease long years ago,[1]
Delighted well with Apuleius
But passing over Cicero;
When in the valley secretly
I wandered lone to watch the swans
And hear their cries above the lake,
Then first my Muse appeared to me.
A sudden flash of inspiration
Made bright the study of a boy,
And there I heard my Muse sing oft
Of childhood pleasures, youth and joy,
Of days heroic, glory past,
And dreams that made my heart beat fast.

2

The world received her with a smile;
My flight of song was swift and brave,
And old Derzhávin gave his blessing
Before the portal of his grave.[2]

. . . .
. . . .
. . . .
. . . .
. . . .
. . . .
. . . .
. . . .
. . . .
. . . .

3

Then I, who held my rights as law,
Took passion for my single guide
And shared my feelings with the crowd,
My young Muse skipping at my side
At each gay feast and wild debate
That stirred the night patrols to rage.
In all our maddest revelries
And joys she shared with us her great
Fine gifts, and like a small bacchante
Sang with my friends across the wine.
Those madcap youths of long ago
With ardor wooed this Muse of mine,
While I exulted in my pride
And praised the darling at my side.[3]

My young Muse skipping at my side
At each gay feast and wild debate

I left the circle of my friends
And fled afar. . . . She followed me.
How often in my lonely travels
Her tenderness and company
Amused me with some wondrous tale!
How often on Caucasian cliffs,
Like fair Lenore,[4] she galloped side
By side with me in moonlight pale!
How often in the midnight mist
Along the dark Crimean shore
She bade me hear the sounding sea
Where nereids murmur evermore,
Where mighty waters sing the praise
Of the Eternal Lord of days.

Thus, far away from city life,
All merriment and feasts forgot,
Among the humble tents of bleak
Moldavia, she cast her lot.
And there she learned the savage tongue
And tribal strains by wandering
With gypsy hosts on rugged ways,
Forsook the airs of godlike song
And turned to primitive refrains.[5]
Then in my garden suddenly
She rose before me as a young
Provincial maid, all modesty,
With pensive sorrow in her glance,
And in her hands a French romance.[6]

6

But now I bring my Muse among
The best of our society,
And here I watch her simple charm
With some concern and jealousy.
Among aristocrats and fops,
Young officers and diplomats,
And ladies proud, my darling walks
And at her chair serenely stops.
Delighted, she observes the scene,
The glitter, women's ballroom dress,
The moving line of guests who greet
The hosts. She notes with eagerness
The men in black who form a frame
Around a lovely miss or dame.

7

She likes their formal conversation,
Their cultivated gracious ways,
Their sense of station, rank and age,
Their pride, their elegance of phrase.
But among this chosen company,
Who is this man who stands apart
In gloomy silence and regards
The passing faces scornfully
As phantoms on a dreary stage?
Is he the prey of grief, or spleen,
Or anguished pride? Who is this man?
From where? Onegin? Do you mean
Eugene? . . . Ah, yes, it's really so.
"When did he get here? Long ago?

Who is this man who stands apart
In gloomy silence and regards
The passing faces scornfully?

216

8

His mood the same, or changed at last?
Still posing, playing the odd fellow?
What is he like now? Do you know?
Conservative and growing mellow?
Or does he play some other role?
A Melmoth, modern patriot,
World citizen, a new Childe Harold,
Quaker, or what fanatic soul?[7]
Or is he just a plain good fellow
Like you and me and all the rest?
He'd better drop outmoded styles;
My counsel's really for the best:
It's time he stopped his tiresome show!"
"Why, do you know him?" "Yes and no."

9

"Then why be merciless? Why take
A harsh, unfavorable view?
Is it because we like to meddle,
To judge, forbid, condemn what's new?
Is it because a soul aflame
Amuses us, or mocks our vain
Self-love and insignificance?
Because free-ranging minds do shame
Our narrow outlook? Because somehow
We take the spoken words for deeds?
Is it because our sluggish minds
Take spite and trifles as our creeds?
Does only mediocrity
Seem fitting, plain to you and me?"

10

Blessed the man who lives his youth,
Who ripens gradually at ease,
Who through the years, unhurt, endures
The world's disdain and enmities;
Who never lets himself be fed
On dreams or shuns the worldly crowd;
Who plays the blade or fop at twenty,
At thirty finds he's settled, wed,
And, if in luck, at fifty has
No sort of debt against his name;
Who quietly, in turn, attains
Promotion, money, rank and fame;
Of whom the talk's no other than
'So'n So is an admirable man.'

11

How sad, alas! to find we've spent
Our youth, the best of life, in vain,
That day by day we played her false,
And that she cheated us again;
That nobler aims and self-denying,
The purer, brighter dreams we dream
Came one by one to slow decay
Like rotting leaves of autumn dying!
How maddening to contemplate
A life more hollow than a rite,
A string of never-ending dinners,
And people ruled by appetite
Whose values govern everywhere,
Whose passions we can never share!

12

Once having been the butt of gossip,
One cannot bear (you will agree)
To be regarded as a freak
By men of true integrity,
Condemned as one both mad and grim,
A monster of satanic pride,
Or as my 'Demon' stand adjudged.[8]
Onegin—I'll return to him—
Who killed his only friend, who lived
Till he was twenty-six a life
Of idleness, without an aim
Beyond himself, without a wife,
Knew nothing he would buckle to—
No work in life he cared to do.

13

Then overcome by restlessness
And discontent in life (I mean
The cross which few can suffer gladly),
He chose to have a change of scene.
At once he left his country seat,
The solitude of wood and field,
Where every day that bloody ghost
He saw again in his retreat.
He started on an aimless journey,—
To find himself his one concern;
Then travel, too, soon filled his heart
With weariness. On his return,
Like Chatsky, at the evenfall
He went directly to a ball.[9]

14

And lo! a flutter stirred the party;
A whisper ran along the hall:
A lady walked into the ballroom
Beside a tall grave general.
She moved unhurried, unaware
She was adored. Not stiff with friends,
Not overbearing in her manner,
Nor wearing a pretentious air;
Without the trick of affectation
So common in society,
All artless and serene she came
Aloof in calm simplicity
Of *comme il faut*. . . . (Shishkóv, berate
Me if you wish: I can't translate.)[10]

15

The ladies pressed a little closer;
Old women smiled as she passed by;
The men saluted, bowing lower,
While passing her, to catch her eye;
Young belles moved slower, dignified
As they came nearer. Prouder, taller
In head and shoulders than the rest
Appeared her husband at her side.
She was not beautiful in features,
And, too, in her attractiveness
There was no trace from head to foot
Of what authorities on dress
In London social sets decry
As *vulgar*. (I refuse to try . . .

16

I dearly love that pithy word,
Although it does not bear translation:
It is still new in social circles,
And has not won much approbation
Except in epigrams). . . . But we
Must watch again our lady where
At a table now she takes her place
With gracious ease, unfeignedly
Enchanting, by Nina Voronskáya,[11]
The Cleopatra of our clime.
Yet you will readily agree
That Nina's beauty, though sublime,
Can not, for all its dazzling pride,
Eclipse the lady at her side.

17

"How can it be?" Onegin wondered,
"She's very like that girl . . . and yet,—
From that dull country place?" Again
He gazed at her through his lorgnette;
Again he studied her as though
Her features dimly brought to mind
Another half-remembered face.
"Your pardon, prince, but do you know
The lady there, in a purple cap,
Next the ambassador of Spain?"
The prince looked narrowly at him:
"You've been away too long, it's plain,
My friend; you're out of touch with life."
"Yes, true, but who is she?" "My wife!"

18

"You're married? Well, that's new to me!
And for how long?" "The second year."
"To whom?" "A Larin." "Who? Tatyána?"
"She knows you then?" "I lived quite near
Their country place,—in former days!"
"Well, come along!" The prince then led
His friend and kinsman to his wife.
She met him with a level gaze....
If she was suddenly surprised
And in her spirit deeply stirred
On seeing him draw near, no look
Betrayed her feelings, nor a word.
Her gentle breeding she preserved;
Her bow,—serene and unreserved.

19

O gods! To seem unmoved, unchanged,
Not flushed with anger, fear, surprise
As he came near! Instead, she looked
At him with clear untroubled eyes.
And though Onegin watched with kind
Attention, yet he could not see
A token of the young Tatyána.
He tried to speak but could not find
A word to say. She asked him when
He had returned and whether he
Had been in their familiar parts,
Then turned to tell her spouse that she
Felt much fatigued, and asked to leave.
Onegin could not as yet believe.

20

Was she, indeed, the same Tatyána
He'd known in that forsaken place
(Before our story had unfolded),
Whom he had lectured face to face,
Impelled by his superior will
And sense of moral excellence?
Could this be she who once had written
The letter that he prizes still—
The letter from that little girl,
Her soul laid bare to him, forlorn
Among her own, whose humble lot
He deemed it was his right to scorn?
Is she the girl from whom he turned
Away, now calm and unconcerned?

21

Onegin left the crowded rooms
And drove off home, but when at last
He fell asleep, his troubled dream
Was sad or sweet about the past.
At noon a note arrived, to invite
Him to the general's that evening.
"My God! To be with her! I'll go!"
He quickly scribbled his polite
Reply. What moved his spirit now?
What witching dream again of old?
What feelings stirred his secret depths,
His heart indifferent and cold?—
Old vanity? vexation? ruth?
Or love, the grave concern of youth?

22

Onegin counts the hours again,
Impatient for the close of day.
The clock strikes ten. He hurries off;
He's flying to her house away.
He's at her door; he enters, weak
With trembling. Tatyána waits alone.
A little while the pair together
In silence sit. He cannot speak.
He fumbles, at a loss to find
The words he wants. Morose, distraught,
He answers absently her questions,
Absorbed by one persistent thought;
He watches stubbornly but she
Remains untroubled, calm, and free.

23

Her husband enters and his coming
Breaks up their awkward *tête-à-tête*;
With Onegin then he starts recalling
Their pranks and jests when first they'd met.
Relaxed, they laugh. New guests meanwhile
Arrive, and soon the conversation
Grows lively, seasoned with the salt
Of worldly mockery and guile.
Tatyána smiles approval when
Small talk gives way to candor, sense,
Without dogmatic affirmations,
Unworthy themes or vain pretense,
When words come quickly, half in fun,
Not meant to nettle anyone.

24

There came the capital's élite
In wealth and fashion—as a rule
The chosen few, but always too
The same inevitable fool.
Some aged ladies, hard of face,
With roses, bonneted, were there;
Some faded marriageable maids,
Unsmiling, all demure in lace;
A foreign diplomat of grave
Appearance, shrewd in state affairs;
One grey-haired scented nobleman
With his familiar jesting airs,
Renowned for saws and mother-wit,
Nowadays ridiculous a bit.

25

Here was an irate carper, hurling
His epigrams with baleful force:
The tea, he cried, was much too sweet;
The ladies, flat; men's style was coarse;
The talked-of novels had no life.
He was annoyed by monograms
To maids-in-waiting,[12] the snow, the war,
The lying papers, and his wife.

. . . .
. . . .
. . . .
. . . .
. . . .
. . . .

26

There was Prolásov,[13] dwarfed in soul
And everywhere for baseness scorned,
Whose features, penciled by St.-Priest,
Too many albums have adorned.
There in command stood, resolute,
The ballroom master, like a print,
Pink-faced just like an Easter cherub,
So nicely groomed, erect, and mute.
There was a foreign traveler
A brazen fellow, starched and proud,
Who by his studied bearing roused
Smiles of amusement from the crowd;
The guests' sly glances were enough
To brand the upstart as a bluff.[14]

27

But my Onegin all that evening
Could think of Tanya only—not
That shy and unaffected maiden
Who seemed to suit an humble lot,
But of this queen, this social star,
Adored, remote, imperious,—
Now ruling on the royal Neva.
O men and sons! You truly are
By birth the progeny of Eve:
The things at hand no longer please,
So constantly the serpent bids
You come beneath the mystic trees;
Forbidden fruit you crave to eat,
Or Eden is no longer sweet.

28

How changed Tatyána, schooled to play
Her role in life! What transformation!
How soon the burden she assumed,
The manner of her galling station!
Who would have thought this regal, cold
Ruler of drawing-rooms had been
But late that artless, lovelorn girl?
Yet he had stirred her heart of old!
It was for him in dark of night
She once did grieve, or, sleepless, lie
With longing in her virgin breast,
And watch the moon sail down the sky,
Dreaming she might beside him spend
Her earthly journey to the end!

29

To love all ages vow submission;
But to the young its raptures bring
A bountiful and wholesome blessing,
Like rains upon a field of spring.
Thus rains of passion at the root
Make new and fair a quickened life,
And nature in its mighty power
Shines gay with flowers, sweet in fruit.
But in our late and sterile years
Of being, when we're growing old,
Love leaves but sorrow in its trail.
Thus stormy winds of autumn cold
Strip every tree with cruel hand
And turn to marsh the fertile land.

30

No doubt, alas! Onegin's fallen
In love with Tanya like a child;
All day, all night, he sorrows, pining,
As lovers do, unreconciled.
And heeding but his heart's despair,
Despite his reason, every day
He drives up to her entrance-hall,
And dogs her like a shadow where'er
She goes. He's glad when he can brush
Her hand or clear for her a way,
When he can throw the downy boa
Around her neck or when he may
Pick up for her the silken shawl
Or handkerchief she has let fall.

31

Yet she appeared indifferent,—
He could keep trying till he died!
She met him amiably at home;
In public she quietly replied
With scarce three words or with a bow
Or failed to notice him at all.
She meant no coquetry, long banned
In best of circles anyhow.
Perhaps she did not care to notice,
But poor Onegin soon began
To sicken, waste away, to look
Consumptive, like a dying man.
His doctors said he must, in short,
Try the cure at a health resort.

32

And yet he stayed, although prepared
To meet his forebears and to say
He'd gladly die. Tatyána seemed
Uncaring,—such is woman's way.
He still had hope she'd understand,
And struggled stubbornly to win her;
Then, bolder than a healthy man,
He wrote her in a trembling hand
A letter eloquent with passion.
He'd thought all letter-writing vain
And profitless, and rightly so,
But now he wrote because with pain
And grief his heart was deeply stirred.
Here is the letter, word for word.

Onegin to Tatyána

I know too well, as I confess
My secret, that your hurt is real.
What cruel scorn at my distress
Your heart must inevitably feel!
What do I ask? What right have I
To say you're all I love on earth?
Perhaps I will but justify
Your anger, hate, and spiteful mirth.

We met—you will recall—by chance,
And when I felt your tender glance,
I did not dare to trust my eyes.
I feared to win your heart just when
I did not wish to lose again

My hateful freedom. I surmise
What kept my life still more apart
From you was Lensky's grievous fate.
From all that's dearest to the heart
I've torn myself away of late.
Estranged, alone with discontent,
I thought I might at least possess
Some peace, some makeshift happiness.
O God, how great my punishment!

But now I long for all my days
To follow you with dedication,
To watch your lips, your gentle gaze
On me, each smile with adoration;
To hear you speak, to feel your whole
Perfection deep within my soul!
To suffer, die—yes, this for me
Were bliss and true felicity!

But such is not my lot. In vain
I follow, seek you everywhere.
Each day, each hour I grudge again,
While I must waste in bored despair
The days allotted me by fate.
And, oh, they are a weary weight!
I have so little time before
Me now; but that my life may last
I must, before the morning's past,
Make sure I'll see you one day more.

I fear my humble supplication
Will anger you, that you will see
Some plot, some cunning strategy
And censure me with indignation.
Believe me, do. If you but knew
My thirst for love, my agitation,
And that each hour I burn anew
In all my helpless desolation!
How much I long to kneel alone
To you, and, weeping at your feet,
Confess my anguish, pray, entreat
Your love and all my past disown;
Instead, pretending self-control,
I must look calm and smile or toy
With words of comfort in my soul,
And watch you in my secret joy! . . .

So be it then: it is too late
To strive, resisting what must be.
I yield my life submissively
To your compassion—and my fate.[15]

33

There is no answer to his letter;
He writes a second, then one more,
But still in vain. Then at a party,
Onegin, just inside the door,
Comes full upon her. Stern, severe,
She does not speak to him nor glance
His way. And, too, like winter frost,
She freezes when he comes too near.
Her lips, unsmiling, hold in check
What indignation of the heart!
He watches long in his despair.
What sign of sympathy or smart,
Confusion, tears? . . . No sign, no trace!
Mute anger only in her face.

34

Perhaps she has a secret fear
Her husband or the world will find
The record of her youthful passion,
Why Onegin has her in his mind. . . .
He curses his stupidity;
He drives away, despairing at
His madness, yet convinced he must
At last forsake society.
Secluded in his lonely study,
He bitterly recalls, of course,
His days of pleasure, how the spleen
Had chased him, held him fast by force,
How sadness snared him for its own
And shut him in his gloom alone.

35

Again he turned to random reading:[16]
He read his Gibbon and Rousseau,
He read Chamfort, Manzoni, Herder,
Bichat, Madame de Staël, Tissot;
He read the works of Fontenelle;
He read the skeptical Pierre Bayle;
Some homebred authors he perused
In any order, as they fell
To him; then almanacs, then journals
Concerned with morals nowadays,
Where I am scolded, while of old
I found sweet madrigals of praise
At times, all in my honor then.—
E sempre bene, gentlemen!

36

But to what end? He scanned the pages
But all his thoughts were far away,
While dreams and sorrows and desires
Came crowding in a strange array.
Though on the printed page at first
He brooded, soon unbidden words
And lines possessed his questing soul,
Aglow with spiritual thirst.
These were mysterious traditions
Of days when hearts were warm and true,
Some stories, threats, and prophecies,
Disjointed dreams without a clue,
Some fairy-tales of lively art
Or letters from a maiden's heart.

37

Onegin sinks in apathy
Of mind and sense by slow degrees,
While fancy, glittering, is spinning
Its motley pageantry. He sees
Before him in a vision dread
A youth lie motionless in snow
As on a hostel bed asleep,
And hears a cry: "Well, he is dead."
He sees old enemies forgotten,
And slanderers and cowards vile,
Sworn friends whom now he holds in scorn,
And sweethearts who, deceiving, smile;
He sees her house . . . and always *she*
By her window-seat—in reverie.

38

Absorbed in such mad dreams, Onegin
Then nearly lost his mind, or worse,
Became a poet in his plight,—
A price, I own, too high for verse.
Indeed, my brainless pupil learned
Somehow the theories and forms
Of poetry,—to be exact,
The way a line of verse is turned.
Indeed he seemed at times a poet
When crooning softly in a trance
The *Benedetta* or *Idol mio*[17]
Before the grate, he'd lose by chance
Upon the ashes carelessly
His slipper or his quarterly.

39

Thus days went by; then warmer air
Waked soft in winter's cold domain
With a new birth. He did not die,
Become a poet, nor go insane.
But, cheered by spring, he quit his chair,
His snug-shut chambers where for weeks
He'd wintered, like a marmot pent,
Behind tight windows in dry air,
And hurried forth one sunny morning
Along the Neva in his sleigh.
The glowing sunshine glistening
On crackling bluish ice-floes lay;
The snows were thawing into slush.
But whither in his headlong rush

40

Did now Onegin speed? You've guessed
The answer. He would no more delay.
To his Tatyána straight my queer
Incorrigible made his way.
He entered, deathly pale; inside,
No footman in the vestibule;
He strode into the great salon,
Then flung another doorway wide,
And sudden halted in confusion.
What filled his spirit with dismay?
He saw the princess, pale, alone,
Downcast, still in her négligé.
She held a letter, and, as she kept
On reading, quietly she wept.

41

And who, on seeing the princess now
In silence grieving, could fail to see
Poor Tanya in that humble figure,
The simple girl she used to be?
Onegin sank before her, low,
Beside himself with wild regret.
She started, then in silence gazed
For long at him without a show
Of anger or surprise. . . . His pale
Drawn features, his unhappy mood,
His sunken eyes, his mute reproach,
With all her soul she understood.
The dream of love of olden days
Shone bright again within her gaze.

42

She did not turn her eyes away;
She did not bid him rise and stand,
Nor from his greedy lips withdraw,
Reproving him, her passive hand.
What were her reveries? Indeed,
The breathless silence lasted long.
Then quietly Tatyána spoke:
"Enough, arise! Now I must plead
And talk with you without reserve.
Onegin, I shall not forget
The hour when, in the garden lane,
By will of destiny we met.
I heard you then in silence, meek;
Today it is my turn to speak.

43

"Onegin, I was younger then,
And better, I believe, than I
Am now. I loved you in my heart.
What was my gain? What, your reply
Except your stern hard looks? For you
It was no novel thing in life
To win a simple girl's first love.
And even now—O God—I rue
My fate, and feel my blood run cold
When I recall your looks again,
That dreadful sermon. . . . I forgive you:
You acted honorably then;
I thank you for the noble part
You chose to play—with all my heart.

44

"In rural loneliness, away
From city fame and idle show,
You did not fancy me.... Why now
Do you today pursue me so?
Because by wealth and rank in life
I move in fashionable circles
And thus deserve your interest?
Because I am a prince's wife?
Because my husband for his wounds
In war found favor at the court?[18]
Because society would relish
My degradation for its sport?
Because to bring a person down
Would win you flattering renown?

45

"I'm crying.... If you can remember
That simple girl, your Tanya still,
Then bear in mind that if I had
My way, that if I had my will,
I should prefer, despite my fears,
Your stinging, scolding speech, your cold
Stern words of days long past to all
This passion, notes, unseemly tears.
For then at least you had the heart
To spare my youth, my indiscreet,
Sad tale of love. But now! Why come
In weakness, kneeling at my feet?
Can you, so true of heart, and kind,
Let selfish ends enslave your mind?

46

"For me, Onegin, all this splendor,
This tinsel of insipid days,
My triumphs here, the social glamor,
This handsome house, and gay soirées,—
What can they mean? I'd gladly yield
This frippery of fancy-balls,
This pomp and glitter, for the shelf
Of books I loved, the open field,
The lane where first I met with you,
Onegin; the garden wild around
Our unpretentious country home,
And for the humble burial-ground
Where now the shady maples wave
Above my dear old nanny's grave.

47

"And happiness came near, so near
For you and me!... But now my fate
Is clear. Perhaps I was unwise,
Indifferent, precipitate:
My mother wept. She pleaded long;
I could not bear the pain I gave her.
My lot was all the same to me....
And so I married, right or wrong.
Onegin, leave me, do; you must.
I know your heart, and that from youth
You've been a man of pride and honor.
I love you,—why conceal the truth?
But I am now another's wife.
I will be faithful all my life."[19]

48

She left. Onegin stood forsaken,
Stood as if struck by lightning's fire,
His heart a tempest of emotions
Engulfed in passion and desire.
He heard outside the silver ring
Of spurs. Tatyána's husband entered.
But here, my reader, we must leave
Onegin to his suffering
And sorrow for a time—for long,
Forever, and forget his fate. . . .
Together we have traveled far
From home. Let's now congratulate
Ourselves on reaching shore at last,
Well pleased our roving days are past.

49

Whoever you may be, dear reader,
My friend or foe, I wish to part
From you and leave you as my friend.
Goodbye! I hope with all my heart
You find whatever you desire
In my small book: fond memories
Of hearty strife, true scenes of life,
Repose from labor, wit, satire,
Or nothing more than faults in grammar.
God grant that you may also find
Some lines that please, some food for dreams,
Some things of moment for your mind,
Some grains of truth. But you and I
Must part, and so again, goodbye.

50

Goodbye, my singular companion!
And you, my true ideal! You, too,
My work of many faithful years,—
My little book! Because of you,
I found some peace on stormy ways,
Sweet talk that friends in freedom share,
The happiness that poets covet.
Ah, many, many fleeting days
Have passed since, in a hazy dream,
I saw young Tanya at a glance
Beside Onegin and perceived
The shape and scope of my romance,
Or thought of what might come to pass
As in a magic crystal glass.

Goodbye! I hope with all my heart
You find whatever you desire
In my small book

51

But some among my closest friends
Who heard my early stanzas read[20]
Are now no more, while others live
Too far away, as Saadi said.[21]
My story's ended, real and true.
But you—my model, Tanya's sweet
Ideal air[22]—I fear to think
How much fate took in taking you!
Happy the man who leaves the feast
Of life betimes, who does not drain
The brimming cup of wine all dry,
Nor crave the whole of life in vain,
Who stops with gladness in his heart,
As I from my Onegin part.

Notes and Comments

Introduction by Belínsky. Few persons have exercised such a far-reaching influence on Russian literature as has the critic Vissarion Belínsky (1811-1848). His historical importance in shaping the social and aesthetic views of Russian youth can scarcely be estimated. To this date, he often is their first teacher and mentor; his authority continues undiminished in matters of enthusiasm, idealism and the progressive temper.

Belínsky was the son of a rural physician who practiced in the province of Penza. His childhood was unhappy; his education, irregular; he died of consumption after years of suffering and privation. However, it was he who, in a series of essays, first revealed the national genius of Pushkin, Lermontov, and Gogol. He was also the first in discerning the seeds of original talent in the early works of Turgenev, Goncharov, Nekrasov, and others. He was a convinced champion of the common people and had faith in their great future.

It is, therefore, only fitting to let Pushkin's contemporary present the portraits of Onegin and Tatyána Larin. The present translation of these two portraits is taken from Belínsky's eighth and ninth essays, published in 1844 and 1845, respectively. Together they form about ninety standard pages. For my translation, I have selected only the significant paragraphs or parts thereof, including whole sentences here and there, to form a continuous running narrative. My aim was to make the subject matter intelligible and succinct as well as continuous, and thus let Belínsky himself appear as the spokesman for Onegin and Tatyána. Therefore, for the reader's enjoyment of the introduction on the printed page through an unbroken account, I have not indicated, by the usual ellipses, the parts omitted from the original.

Epigraph and Dedication. The French epigraph, now usually printed before Pushkin's dedication, was written by the poet himself. It is presented as something extracted from a private letter: "Besides being thoroughly vain, he was possessed by that kind of singular pride which makes one confess with equal indifference both his good and evil actions, from a sense of superiority existing perhaps only in his imagination." It is a fitting description of the Onegin type. The dedication is addressed to P. A. Pletnev, the poet's publisher and friend.

Numbers in parentheses, found in the eight chapters, indicate stanzas omitted by the poet. In preparing the text for the press,

Pushkin occasionally omitted one or more stanzas or left some of them unfinished; he did not go to the trouble of renumbering the stanzas.

CHAPTER ONE

Epigraph for Chapter One is by Prince Pyótr Andréyevich Vyázemsky (1792-1878), a friend and contemporary of Pushkin; a minor poet and keen critic. The quotation is from his poem "First Snow" and shows that Pushkin intended to make his 'novel in verse' a serious critique of his age.

1. *Stanza 1.* The first line alludes to the opening statement in Ivan Krylóv's fable: "The Ass and the Peasant" (1818). The ass was the soul of the highest moral principles. It was for that reason allowed to guard the garden from raids by crows and sparrows, a matter which should have not been entrusted to it despite its private virtues. Krylov had in mind the indifferent and wasteful management of feudal estates by their aristocratic owners, as exemplified by Onegin's own uncle (ch. 2, stanza 3).

2. *Stanza 2.* "Ruslán and Lyudmíla" are the names of the hero and heroine of Pushkin's first narrative poem, published in 1820, a mock-heroic fairy tale in verse.

3. *Stanza 2.* Line 14, a flippant, caustic reference to his transfer from the capital to Bessarabia in the South as a punishment for his subversive poems and epigrams.

4. *Stanza 5.* Onegin is here characterized as a well-read young man but pedantic. In Pushkin's day, *pedant* described one who is forward, opinionated, presumptuous, independent in mind, critical of conditions.

5. *Stanza 6.* Books of anecdotes, past and present, were common at the end of the 18th century. They had some historic value, but were short on the side of accuracy.

6. *Stanza 12.* Faublas is the hero of a novel by Louvet de Couvray (1760-1797) entitled "La Vie du Chevalier de Faublas." Faublas spent a lifetime in amatory adventures.

7. *Stanza 15.* Hat à la Bolivar: A high hat with a broad brim, named in honor of Simon Bolivar, hero of South American independence.

8. *Stanza 15.* Breguet, a pocket watch which strikes, a repeater, named after Parisian watchmaker, Abraham Louis Breguet (1747-1823).

9. *Stanza 16.* P. P. Kavérin (1794-1855). Hussar officer, friend of Pushkin; a popular dandy of the day who combined high living with intellectual interests.

10. *Stanza 16.* Talon was a famous French restaurant in Petersburg. "Comet" champagne was a wine of 1811 known for its excellence; it owed its name to the comet that appeared in that year. "Strasbourg" pies, later referred to as pastry, were made of goose liver; imported in individual packages to keep them fresh.

11. *Stanza 17.* Moïna was the name of the heroine in V. A. Ózerov's tragedy, "Fingal."

12. *Stanza 18.* This stanza celebrates the development of Russian drama and ballet based on native themes, in close imitation of the French classics of Corneille, Racine, Molière. ÐENIS I. VONVÍSIN (1745-1792) was a noted writer of comedies. "The Brigadier" procured him the favor of Catherine II, but his best satiric comedy was "The Minor." J. B. KNYAZHNÍN (1742-1791) had the reputation of a Russian Racine as writer of comedies and tragedies. V. A. ÓZEROV (1770- 1816) was known for his classical sentimental tragedies, such as "Fingal" and "Dmitri of the Don." The celebrated beautiful actress, E. Semyónova (1786-1849) played in them; she was also the greatest performer in the role of Phèdre. P. A. KATÉNIN (1792-1853) was a friend of Pushkin; a minor poet, translator of Racine and Corneille, prominent in discussions of classicism and romanticism. Prince A. A. SHAKHOVSKÓY (1777-1846) was author of many comedies; director of the Imperial Theatre in Petersburg, an opponent of romanticism. CHARLES-LOUIS DIDELÓT (1767-1837) was the balletmaster and choreographer; he taught Istómina. He was also author of ballets on themes from Pushkin's narrative poems.

13. *Stanza 20.* A. I. Istómina (1799-1848) was one of Didelót's ballerinas, famous for her beauty and art. She danced in the ballets based on Pushkin's "The Caucasian Prisoner" and "Ruslán and Lyudmíla."

14. *Stanza 23.* Pushkin was not ironical in describing Onegin as a philosopher at age 18: He had in mind a youth of

vague, speculative chat. Serious mature thinkers were then known as "wisdom lovers."

15. *Stanza 24.* Line 11. To this passage Pushkin attached a note quoting Rousseau who in his "Confessions" relates his encounter with Frédéric-Melchior Grimm, the Parisian critic, encyclopedist, and correspondent of Catherine II. Pushkin wrote: "Grimm was in advance of his age. Nowadays, throughout cultured Europe, nails are cleaned with a special little brush."

16. *Stanza 25.* P. Y. Chaadáyev (1794-1856) was widely known for his elegance of dress and manners. Pushkin's friend, a representative of Westernism and Catholicism; author of famous "Philosophic Letters."

17. *Stanza 26.* The Academic Lexicon was published in six volumes only in 1789-1794. It was conservative, opposed to use of foreign words.

18. *Stanza 33.* This famous digression on shapely legs refers to Maria Rayévsky, daughter of General N. N. Rayévsky in whose company Pushkin visited the Caucasus and Crimea. Maria, who was 16 then, reported in her diary that the poet normally falls in love with every pretty woman, that he idealizes too much, that he is only in love with his Muse. She later married prince Volkónsky, the Decembrist, and won fame for her devotion in sharing her husband's exile in Siberia. No doubt Pushkin had in mind her exalted sense of duty in drawing the character of Tatyána.

19. *Stanza 38.* In chapter one we have the environment which was the source of 'blues,' a state of mental and spiritual weariness that plagued the privileged classes of society. In the following chapters, Onegin was bound to come face to face with the actual problems of life and be tried as a man. The 'blues' was a state of almost total indifference, without men's commitment to past, present, or future.

20. *Stanza 42.* Bentham and J. B. Say were popular in the progressive circles, especially with the future Decembrists. Say dedicated the second edition of his famous work to Tsar Alexander I at the time the Russian armies entered Paris (1814). The work was originally not passed by Napoleon's censors.

21. *Stanza 48.* Pushkin has reference to a pseudo-archaic poem,

"To the Goddess of the Neva" by A. N. Muravyóv; it described the ecstatic poet leaning against the granite walls.

22. *Stanza 49.* The reference is to Lord Byron, poet of Albion.

23. *Stanza 50.* Line 4 hints at his plans to flee abroad from Odessa where the poet was a semi-exiled man.

24. *Stanza 50.* Line 10 refers to Pushkin's colorful description of his Ethiopian ancestor and his distinguished career. On his mother's side, the poet was of African descent. His great-grandfather, Abram Petrovich Hannibal, was lured away at the age of eight from the shores of Africa and taken to Constantinople. The Russian envoy rescued him and sent him as a gift to Tsar Peter the Great. The Tsar attended to his education and promotion in the service; he also ennobled him and had him married to a lady of the court.

25. *Stanza 56.* The difference between Byron and Pushkin has been pointed out by Belínsky. Pushkin felt all the sufferings of civilized man but he also had a firm faith in the saving qualities of men and society, a faith lacking in Lord Byron.

26. *Stanza 57.* Salghir is a stream in the Crimea. The poet refers to the heroines of his two narrative poems: "The Prisoner of the Caucasus" and "The Fountain of Bakhchi-Saray."

CHAPTER TWO

Epigraph. Pushkin bewails his life of rural isolation and loneliness in the village (*rus*) of Mikháilovskoye. The ancient name for Russia was *Rus*, now used mainly in poetry or declamatory prose. For over two years all of Russia was for the poet a prison,—a small village in the backwoods.

1. *Stanza 4.* Onegin is presented as a social reformer in that he substituted a light quit-rent (*obrok*, in money or kind) for the yoke of coercive labor. By the law of 1797 serf labor on the landlord's estate was limited to three days per week, but it was not enforced.

2. *Stanza 5.* "Formasón" is a corruption of "franc maçon." Among the half-educated, the Masons were greatly feared and regarded as adherents of Anti-Christ. Pushkin joined

the Ovid lodge in Kishinev. In 1821 Masonic lodges were prohibited by Tsar Alexander I.

3. *Stanza 6.* The University of Göttingen was famous for its liberalism, but regarded by some as a hotbed of depravity and godlessness. A. Kunítsyn, Pushkin's teacher at the Lyceum, was influenced by Kant; he held, in his work on Natural Law, 1818, that "no one has the right to use a fellow-man as an object or means for his own advantage." He was therefore dismissed from his professorship in 1821. Another teacher, A. I. Galich, a follower of Schelling, was forced to resign his lectureship at the University of Petersburg at the same time.

4. *Stanza 12.* The reference is to a popular aria from the opera, "The Dnepr Mermaid" by N. S. Krasnopólsky, a translation from the German "Das Donauweibchen" by Karl Heusler; music by F. Kauer. The aria was extremely popular for over two decades.

5. *Stanza 24.* The name Tatyána was either archaic or common. Its later popularity was partly due to Pushkin's heroine. "Sweet-sounding Greek names, as, for example, Agathon, Philat, Theodora, Thecla, etc. are only in use with us among the common people." (Pushkin's note.)

6. *Stanza 32.* The development of old Larina from a sensitive young girl into a strict mistress was a familiar experience. She shaved peasant locks: it means that she had the power to send her serfs into the army, an act of extreme cruelty, considering that 25 years of service was common at that time.

7. *Stanza 33.* Sentimental young girls had the habit of writing their sentiments in albums, not in ink but in blood as a mark of love and attachment.

8. *Stanza 35.* Line 11 refers to a field flower known as 'dawn' flower, a name given in honor of Easter and Resurrection. Living rooms were often decorated with lovage on Trinity Sunday in memory of the dead. Pushkin once informed his censor, I. Snegirov, that in some parts of the country it was customary to brush off parental graves with lovage flowers, the symbol of dawn and Easter,—to cleanse the eyes of the dead.

9. *Stanza 37.* Pushkin's own notation reads: "Poor Yorick! Hamlet's exclamation over the fool's skull (see Shakespeare

and Sterne)." This notation does not mean that Lensky is ironically applying the clown's name to Brigadier Larin. He respected Larin's memory, revered him for the Ochákov medal bestowed for bravery in action by Catherine II.

10. *Stanza 38.* This stanza represents Pushkin's rationalist view of life and death, free from romantic and religious mysticism. It shows the influence of Holbach on the poet's generation.

CHAPTER THREE

1. *Stanza 3.* The concluding six lines, deleted by Pushkin, show his absorbing interest in minute rural details: "Country people like to eat at all hours of the day. With folded arms, crowded beside each door, the housemaids gathered to stare at their new neighbor. In the yard, the horseboys judged the horses point by point."

2. *Stanza 5.* "Svetlána," heroine of a poem by Pushkin's friend and mentor, the poet Zhukóvsky; published in 1812. Influenced by Bürger's "Lenore."

3. *Stanza 9.* Julie Wolmar, the heroine of Rousseau's "La Nouvelle Héloïse." Gustav de Linar: the hero of a novel by Juliana von Krüdener. Malek-Adehl: the hero of a novel by Mme Cottin. Goethe's "Werther" was first translated in 1782.

4. *Stanza 10.* Julie is the heroine of Rousseau's novel. Clarissa, the heroine of Richardson's Clarissa Harlowe. Delphine, the title heroine of Mme. de Staël's novel.

5. *Stanza 12.* The romantic tale, "The Vampire," 1819, by Byron's private secretary, John William Polidori; the novel was at one time ascribed to Byron. "Melmoth, the Wanderer," a production of genius by C. R. Maturin. Charles Nodier's "Jean Sbogar" appeared in 1818; prohibited in Russia because the hero was a robber. "The Corsair" is Byron's, of course. Pushkin opposed the moralistic novels and made fun of their poetic clumsiness.

6. *Stanza 27.* The reference is to the Moscow journal known as the "Moral Mentor" or "Well-Intentioned" (Blagonamérenny). It was published by the novelist and fabulist, A. E. Izmailov, but it seldom appeared on time.

7. *Stanza 28.* No special identification intended here; Pushkin

means all men and women of limited education, bad tastes and manners.

8. *Stanza 29.* H. F. Bogdanóvich (1743-1802) is remembered for his story in verse, "Dushenka," inspired by La Fontaine's "Psyché."

9. *Stanza 29.* De Parny, French writer of erotic lyrics (1753-1814).

10. *Stanza 30.* E. A. Baratýnsky (1800-1814) was the most important poet of Pushkin's circle of friends. The reference is to Eda, the Finnish heroine who was in love with a Russian officer.

11. *Stanza 31.* "Freischütz," a romantic opera by C. M. von Weber, first presented in Dresden in 1819. Very popular in Russia.

12. *Stanza 32.* Thin wafers were used for sealing letters; no envelopes with glue were available at that time.

CHAPTER FOUR

Pushkin chose his epigraph from "Considérations de Révolution Française" by Mme. de Staël, 1818. She quoted her father, Jacque Necker, from a statement he had made to Mirabeau.

1. *Stanza 7.* Pushkin is here referring to his letter written from Kishinev in 1822 to his brother: "The less one loves a woman, the greater is one's chance of possession. But such enjoyments are worthy of old baboons of the 18th century." Such were also Onegin's opinions, as expressed in stanza 9.

2 *Stanza 17.* Onegin is old-fashioned in his views of a woman's integral personality or woman's rights in love and marriage. The poet emphasizes that he delivered an honest sermon,—for the moment.

3. *Stanza 30.* Count Fyódor Petróvich Tolstoy (1783-1873) famous as sculptor, engraver, medallion-maker. He was also vice-president of the Petersburg Academy of Arts. His cousin, Nickolai Tolstoy, was the father of Count Leo Tolstoy.

4. *Stanza 30.* E. A. Baratynsky (see note 10 for chapter 3).

5. *Stanza 31.* N. M. Yazykov (1803-1846), a lyricist contemporary with Pushkin, later a Slavophile, an author of

unfulfilled promise. The reference does not imply a similarity between Lensky and Yazykov.

6. *Stanza 32.* Line 1 has reference to Wilhelm Küchelbecker who attacked elegies (meaning also lyrics) as a romantic form and defended the odes as superior poetry because of the element of rapture (*vostorg*) in the composition. Pushkin charged that the ode is a low form of composition, that serenity (*spokoistviye*) was the chief condition of highest art.

7. *Stanza 32.* In line 10 the allusion is to emblems for ode, drama and satire.

8. *Stanza 33.* Ivan Dmítriev (1760-1837) was the author of the famous witty satire, entitled "Other People's Opinions," published in 1795. His satire helped to make an end to ode-writing.

9. *Stanza 35.* Pushkin would hold himself aloof from all partizanship. He considered that the main thing is not the literary genre but quality of work. For instance, he was inspired by his old nurse, Arina Rodiónovna, to write folk tales in verse; inspired also by Shakespeare to write his "Boris Godunov" which he read to friends.

10. *Stanza 37.* Lines 9-11 refer to Gulnare, the heroine of "The Corsair," and to Byron's swimming the Hellespont.

11. *Stanza 37.* Line 13 shows 1½ lines omitted, also one whole stanza (38) excluded from the author's text. The omitted parts describe Onegin as an insufferable neighbor, regarded as immoral and insane, because "he wore a Russian smock, then a scarf of silk for a girdle, a Tartar coat, unbuttoned, and a high round hat."

11. *Stanza 41.* Pushkin's unfriendly critics expressed surprise that he referred to common peasant girls as 'maidens,' a name reserved only for gentle young ladies. [In chapter 5, stanza 28, he refers to young ladies as wenches.]

13. *Stanza 43.* Dominique de Pradt (1759-1837). He was archbishop of Malines, diplomat, and Napoleon's chaplain; popular as political essayist.

14. *Stanza 46.* Aÿ, a champagne from the Marne region; poetic Aÿ is associated with youth and love by reason of its whispering foam.

15. *Stanza 47.* The dusk hour 'twixt wolf-and-dog' is Pushkin's witty translation of the French 'entre chien et loup.'

16. *Stanza 50.* August Heinrich Lafontaine is on record as author of over 150 novels about sentimental domestic life. A German Huguenot.

CHAPTER FIVE

Epigraph is taken from Zhukóvsky's famous ballad "Svetlána." The stanzas devoted to fortune-telling in Pushkin's poem are modeled directly on the ballad. Like Svetlána, Tatyána is represented as a young woman 'Russian in her soul.'

1. *Stanza 3.* In line 9 the other poet who glorified winter
2. snow is Prince P. A. Vyázemsky. For other delights of the winter season, Pushkin directs the reader to E. A. Baratynsky, especially his "Eda."
3. *Stanza 4.* It was common then to read fortunes on the night of January 5th, on the eve of the Lord's baptism. Tatyána shared the beliefs and superstitions of the common people (see stanzas 5 to 8). The 'dish songs' (*podblyudny pesni*) used during Holy Nights (*svyatki*) for purposes of divination continued from Christmas (Nativity) to Twelfth-Night (Baptism).
4. *Stanza 8.* Rites like the rings-in-a-dish were initiated by wax-casting, by pouring molten wax in a bowl of cold water and then covering with a cloth. The drawn rings signified fame for the lucky ones. In this stanza it is an augury of death. The 'cat song' foretells marriage: "Tomcat calls his pussy to sleep in the stove-niche" is a prophesy of a wedding.
5. *Stanza 9.* The girl expects to see her future husband in the mirror, also to hear his name from the man she first accosts. In Tatyána's case, it was Agafón (Agathon), a typically common peasant name.
6. *Stanza 10.* The bath-houses were known as meeting places for the spirits; no icons were hung on their walls. Tatyána makes the same preparations that Svetlána does in Zhukovsky's ballad. She expects to see her future husband reflected in the mirror and to see his spirit opposite her at the table.
7. *Stanza 10.* Lel' is supposed to be the goddess of love and marriage in ancient Slavonic mythology. Actually, it is simply

a refrain word from an old folk song. (*Lel'* is connected with the word *leleyat'*, meaning 'to fondle' or 'to soothe').

8. *Stanza 22.* Martyn Zadeka (real name is Zadek) was probably a Pole or a Czech; his original work is traced to the 17th century. First Russian translation was from the German, in 1770. Pushkin maintained that books on fortune-telling were published in Russia under the imprint of Zadeka, who was not their author.

9. *Stanza 23.* A list of trashy contemporary literature familiar
10. to Tatyána: "Malvine" a novel by Mme Sophie Cottin, pub-
11. lished in Russian translation in 1816-18. "Petriads" were epic glorifications of Tsar Peter the Great, 1812, by S. A. Stikhmátov and A. N. Grusíntsev. The French novelist, Jean Marmontel (1723-1799) was widely read in Russian translations. The hackneyed fables were by A. Izmáilov or A. Nakhímov, noted for their vulgarisms.

12. *Stanza 25.* The 'rosy fingers of the sun' is a parody on well-known lines from Lomonósov's ode on the "Coronation of Elizabeth Petrovna," 1746.

13. *Stanza 26.* Buyánov figures in "The Dangerous Neighbor" by Vassíli L. Pushkin, the poet's uncle, whence the statement "my own first cousin."

14. *Stanza 27.* Monsieur Triquet's so-called original song was taken from a popular romance by Charles Dufresny de la Rivière (1648-1724), famous in his day for comedies, novels, and especially songs.

15. *Stanza 32.* Zizi was the pet name of Evpráksia Wulf (1810-1883), one of the daughters of Mme. Osipova, a neighbor of Pushkin. Zizi was a lively attractive girl of 15; she was very clever in making hot punch or *zhonka*: sweetened drink flavored with fruit juices, spices, mixed with wine or liquor. Pushkin dedicated to her the short poem, "Should Hopes Deceive You."

16. *Stanza 40.* The reference is to Francesco Albani (1578-1660), baroque painter famous for his mythological subjects, nymphs, and graces. Pushkin admired him for his precise details.

CHAPTER SIX

Epigraph, from Petrarch's "Canzone," may be rendered as follows: "There, where days are brief and cloudy, a people is born who have no fear of death."

1. *Stanza 5.* The reference is to Very Frères, a celebrated restaurant in Paris, famous in the first half of the 19th century. The episode about Zaretsky's imprisonment seems to have been invented, but not his traits of character and behavior.
2. *Stanza 11.* The line about public opinion ('the stupid judgment of the crowd') is derived from Griboyédov's dramatic work, "Woe From Wit," Act IV, Scene 10.
3. *Stanza 20.* Baron Anton Delvig (1798-1831) was a minor lyric poet; a schoolmate of Pushkin from the Lyceum days; a lifetime intimate friend.
4. *Stanza 22.* Pushkin's treatment of Lensky as a poet is both serious and humorous, but tolerant in all respects.
5. *Stanza 23.* Lensky's elegies were derived from such sources as Parny, A. Chenier, Lamartine, Charles Millvoye, Nicolas Gilbert, all of them contemporary French elegiac poets; also from Russian translations and imitations.
6. *Stanza 25.* Lepage, name of famous gunsmith.
7. *Stanza 26.* Zarétsky was precise about codes of honor relating to duels. Onegin, in his disdainful mood, departed from the traditional rules by bringing his personal servant as his second.

CHAPTER SEVEN

1. *Stanza 4.* V. A. Levshin (1746-1826), author of a number of books on rural husbandry. (Pushkin's note.)
2. *Stanza 10.* According to Belínsky, Pushkin bewailed the romantic poverty of Lensky and his consequent immaturity in the affairs of life: "His heart, though affectionate, was ignorant. His joys and sorrows were the creatures of his own imagination. . . . He embellished her (Olga) with virtues and perfections; he ascribed to her thoughts and feelings which she had not and cared little for."

3. *Stanza 22.* In Pushkin's rough draft we have a fairly long list of books in keeping with Onegin's interests. In the final version Pushkin reduced the list to Byron and 2 or 3 contemporary novels. One was certainly Benjamin Constants 'Adolphe' translated by Prince Vyázemsky in 1816. Maturin's 'Melmoth' was mentioned in ch. 3, stanza 12. The other two authors mentioned are Chateaubriand and Sénancour.

4. *Stanza 24.* In wondering whether Onegin is a freak, a man to fear, or a parody upon his age, Tatyána is unconsciously repeating to herself the gossip current among the rural neighbors who regarded him as a very queer and 'dangerous' man. (ch. 2, stanzas 4-5).

5. *Stanza 37.* Peter's Palace, outside Moscow in Pushkin's day, was built by Catherine II. Napoleon found refuge there from the fires ravaging Moscow, 1812.

6. *Stanza 38.* The gates "with lions' stony jaws" were part of the aristocratic English Club; a decorative sculpture favored by the wealthy. The building is now occupied by the Museum of the Revolution.

   In line 14, we have Pushkin's statement that the church crosses were 'black with flocks of daws.' Metropolitan archbishop Philaret complained that the line was impious and blasphemous, to which the censor replied that it was the duty of the police department to keep the daws off the cupolas and the golden crosses, that neither the poet nor the censor was responsible for the irreverence shown by the daws. The Tsar's Minister of Internal Affairs, the powerful Count Benckendorff, gently hinted to the archbishop of the futility of interference in matters of that sort.

7. *Stanza 49.* The 'youthful archivists' were young men of the nobility serving in the Moscow State Archives of Foreign Affairs, sinecures reserved for the privileged youths but involving no serious responsibility or work. At the time of Tatyána's appearance in Moscow, a few of them formed a discussion group concerned with the philosophic systems of Kant, Fichte, and Schelling. They were idealistic, pretentious, and naturally exclusive.

8. *Stanza 49.* Prince P. A. Vyázemsky (1792-1878) was Pushkin's intimate friend, a serious, keen, discriminating critic;

259

minor poet; a man of wealth and taste. Pushkin wishes to say that he quickly guessed the true character of that simple country girl, Tatyána Larin.

9. *Stanza 50.* The periphrastic style of the stanza, so foreign to Pushkin's realism, is one of conscious choice, intended at this point as a satire on the privileged classes among whom Tatyána found herself. (Humorously, good-naturedly, the poet shakes off the 18th century of classicism in the concluding stanza 55.)

10. *Stanza 52.* The first four lines form a parody of a poem by S. Bobrov, author of "Taurida," 1798. The bright stars were the self-centered vain belles of the society lampooned in stanza 51. For real beauty and steady light the poet has in mind the 18-year-old Alexandra Korsakova. The poet's style fits the romantic mood recollected in tranquility, a mood smilingly and gladly thrown off in the concluding coda.

CHAPTER EIGHT

1. *Stanza 1.* Reference to Pushkin's adolescent years spent in the Lyceum at Tsárskoye Seló, an exclusive boarding school near Petersburg established by Tsar Alexander I. Pushkin was entered with the first class in 1811. Stanzas 1 to 5 are autobiographical.

2. *Stanza 2.* Stanza left unfinished in the final edition: ten lines deleted by Pushkin. In 1815, at a public ceremony at the Lyceum, young Pushkin read his poem, "Recollections of Tsárskoye Seló," in the presence of the venerable poet, G. A. Derzhávin (1743-1816).

3. *Stanza 3.* Pushkin refers here to poems composed in the Lyceum and in the first years after his graduation (1817-1820). He was exceedingly popular. According to Tsar Alexander I, Pushkin 'has deluged Russia with shocking verses. All the youths are learning them by heart.'

4. *Stanza 4.* Lenore: The heroine of Gottfried August Bürger's celebrated romantic ballad by that title.

5. *Stanza 5.* The poet refers his readers to his narrative poems,
6. "The Captive of the Caucasus," "The Fountain of Bakhchi-

Sarai," "The Gypsies," and the early parts of the "Eugene Onegin" itself.

7. *Stanza 8.* We are now on the eve of the Decembrist rebellion. Onegin is not a freak or simply dangerous. His features are now more complex, representative of new aspirations, ideas, restlessness, illusions. The reflective minds are trying to discover the sensibilities under the various masks. In stanzas 9 to 11, Pushkin shows himself on the side of the questing idealism of the new generation. He defends Onegin's right to live his own life, to feel and to think afresh, and demands sympathy for his hero. He defends him against irresponsible gossip.

8. *Stanza 12.* "The Demon," 1823: In his days of youth, joy and aspiration, the poet is visited by the evil genius of disillusionment who poisons his heart, whispers that all is illusion and mocks at ideals of love and freedom.

9. *Stanza 13.* Chatsky is the hero of Alexander Griboyédov's famous comedy, "Woe From Wit," 1824.

10. *Stanza 14.* Vice admiral A. S. Shishkóv held various posts including that of Minister of Education. He was a purist; violent in linguistic debates in which he upheld the use of old Slavonic words and opposed foreign phrases and innovations. He feared that the use of French words will inevitably bring in French ideas.

11. *Stanza 16.* The name of Nina Voronskáya is fictitious. Commentators agree that the society beauty Pushkin had in mind was countess E. M. Zavadóvskaya (1807-1874), famous for her 'marble' beauty. To her he dedicated the poem, 'The Beauty.'

12. *Stanza 25.* The irate gentleman was count G. K. Modern, but the details seem to have been invented for comic effects. The monogram of the royal family, a decoration in the form of jeweled initials, was a badge of honor bestowed upon ladies-in-waiting. The allusion is to two ladies, Alexandra Osipovna Rosset and Stephanie Radziwill.

13. *Stanza 26.* Prolásov has been proposed as the target for the pen of St. Priest. Prolásov never existed (the name means

14. 'social climber'). The description is now applied to Andrei I. Sabúrov (1797-1866), later director of Imperial theatres, a man noted for his conservatism and obstinacy. (The

evidence is not conclusive that Sabúrov is meant, but there are caricatures of him by St. Priest.) Count Emmanuel de Saint-Priest was the son of a French émigré, admired and feared for his drawings and caricatures. In the same stanza, Pushkin presents other social climbers making a career in society (also in stanza 24), all in sharp distinction from Tatyána's aristocratic circle of friends (st. 23).

15. *Onegin's Letter* seems modeled on Tatyána's letter. There are a number of parallel expressions, recalling the influence of Rousseau. There is more passion and more egotism in Onegin's letter. He expects Tatyána to feel a kind of remorseful joy in response to his declaration of love.

16. *Stanza 35.* Onegin's reading was among works of leading authors. NICHOLAS DE CHAMFORT (1741-1794), author of novels and plays, but best known for his aphorisms (for instance, the famous 'Guerre aux châteaux, paix aux chaumières'). MANZONI was the leader of Italian romanticists (1784-1873). MARIE F. X. BICHAT (1771-1802) was a French physician and physiologist; he wrote a treatise on nature. SIMON TISSOT was a Swiss doctor and author of popular medical works, (1728-1797). PIERRE BAYLE (1647-1706), French freethinker and skeptical philosopher, whose famous dictionary was one of the classics of French literature, 1696. BERNARD DE FONTENELLE, (1657-1757), popular philosopher, poet, exponent of rationalism. HERDER (1744-1803), German man of letters and philosopher.

17. *Stanza 38.* "Idol mio, piu pace non ho," a popular refrain by Vincenzo Gabussi. "Benedetta sia la madre" was a popular Venetian barcarolle. Pushkin heard Mme A. P. Kern sing Kozlov's serenade to the tune of the "Benedetta."

18. *Stanza 44.* The description of Tatyána's husband as grave, dignified, wounded in wars, has created the impression that he was an old man. The general was stout but not old. He and Onegin were friends and playfellows in the past; their families were related. Onegin was now 28, and the general was perhaps six years older. Rayevsky, a friend of the poet, was a general at 29. Many young officers achieved high rank during the Napoleonic War.

19. *Stanza 47.* Onegin and Tatyána are recognized as progenitors of a great succession of characters of Russian realism,

—in the fiction of Lermontov, Goncharov, Turgenev, Tolstoy, Chekhov, and others. In many novels the self-centered Onegin type (ch. 7, st. 22: inordinately visionary, disdainful, with embittered minds at sea seething in vain activity) comes face to face with the calm self-command and moral greatness of the Tatyána type. The novelist Goncharov has succinctly presented the case of men of the dead past, living outside the future, in the words of his Olga addressing Ilya Oblómov: "I realized that I was loving in you only what I wished you to have—only the future of my dream that was so dear to me." Pushkin's special greatness, as stern and objective as Fate, is that he treats Onegin with sympathy but without pity, and his beloved Tatyána with reverence, because of her truthfulness and candor, but without a reward for her virtues, redeemed by the sadness of her loveless life accepted unquestionably without fear. "Love is life," says Goncharov's Olga, "and life is a duty, an obligation; consequently love also is a duty. God has sent me that duty, and has intended that I perform it."

20. *Stanza 51.* Pushkin spent eight years of his most creative life in writing "the poem in verse." It was begun in Kishinev on the evening of May 9th, 1823, and completed at the Boldino estate on September 25th, 1830. Onegin's letter to Tatyána was done in October, 1831. The work was published as a whole in 1833 and again in 1837, ten days before the poet's death.

21.   A veiled allusion to friends executed for their part in the Decembrist revolt of 1825, and to those living 'too far away' as exiles in Siberia. Saadi is the great Persian poet of the 13th century, Muslihud-Din-Saadi.

22.   A few ladies are mentioned by contemporaries as the models, although Pushkin's Tatyána was not an exact copy of one person.